Closing 100% of Your Fitness Consultations

3 Secret Steps System Every Fitness Professional, Personal Trainer and Gym Owner Must Know To Succeed

Thank you Cuya Ermia
for the mentorship
Over the years.
Tony Deoleo
7/25/2020

Tony Deoleo

ISBN: 978-1-952263-59-0

Dedication

I dedicate this book to my beautiful wife, Lorie Deoleo, who has been there through my entrepreneur career with her unconditional support through the challenging times.

I also dedicate this book to my friend and family, Larry Warren, who inspired this book when his life-long fight ended with diabetes complications.

And finally, I dedicate this book to my inspiring fitness client of 10 + years and friend Leslie Charleson. She, with her hard work and dedication to her fitness, was also a great source of inspiration in creating this amazing contribution book.

A special collaboration with Mr. Dee Black.

Acknowledgment

I would like to thank everyone who helped me bring my vision to reality in the form of this book. I am grateful for everyone who supported me and those who evaluated every aspect of this book. I thank Mr. Karl O'Neil, my inspiring fitness client of over 10 years Leslie Charleson, Yudelka Weeks for her inspiration with her entrepreneurial spirit, and Mr. Jimmie Jackson for his mentorship over the past few years. I would also like to acknowledge my initial transcriptionist Alaa Jameel Albarbari, Michael Davis, Chino Bravo, Franco Giordanengo, Josiah Krist Pinagayao, Ricky De Mesa, Kiki Melendez, visionary fitness advocate Tim D Keightley, and the entire team for their patience and belief in my project.

Thank you.

About the Author

Hi, I am Tony Deoleo, International Fitness Expert and Celebrity Fitness Trainer in the Capital of fitness Los Angeles California.

I have had the privilege of personally developing more than 1000 Fitness Professionals and conducting over 40,000 fitness consultations over the past 20 years, followed by training General Managers, Gym Owners, Fitness Managers, and personal trainers in my speaking career on how to sell personal training services at the point of sales and at fitness consultations.

I noticed that too many new trainers start their personal training career with a very low chance of succeeding over the years because they cannot simply close the personal training sale to convert those fitness consultations into your new Clients!

So, I came up with a perfect three secret steps system that I have used to develop over 30 teams and close 100% of our fitness consultations and bring between 1.2 to 1.0 million dollars in personal training revenue per year to more than 20 fitness club in the USA as well as consulting clubs in Asia in the past 20 years.

I decided to make this book available for every one of you to help you achieve great success in your fitness career and help your clients achieve their fitness goals while making a living for you and your family and contributing to the success of your fitness club in addition to enjoying the benefits of a wonderful career as a fitness professional and saving lives through fitness!

Preface

Fitness is a lot more than just sweating long hours at the gym or starving yourself of all the good food you could eat. Tony Deoleo, in this book, talks to his readers one-on-one, manifesting the idea of living a healthy and happy life. With the workout and training programs discussed in the book, he reaches out not just to the customers but specifically the trainers who wish to expand their fitness program career. From entering into the gym to retaining the client, and to assessing their BMIs to recommend the best workout plans, this book is a plethora of information for novice and professional trainers.

Contents

Page Left Blank Intentionally

Chapter 1
Introduction

Dear fitness-minded professionals, are you still figuring out ways to make that 6-figure salary? Or are you about to give up on the hope that you could make it? Well, don't! You wouldn't like it if any of your clients gave up their fitness goals, would you?

It's good if you are still looking for ideas. Curiosity is the first step toward the bountiful journey of success. However, if you are on the verge of giving up, then you have come to the right place. In this book, I will share solutions to your professional problems, so you are back on the success track.

Let's explore the road to success by learning and growing with each step. At least once in your career, you must have wondered how some people from the same field can bag hundreds of thousands of dollars per annum, while you are stuck in second gear. Maybe you wish that you had the same foolproof and reliable sales, marketing, and business strategies. Or perhaps you think the secret lies in the clientele, and you wonder how you can retain your clients.

So what are the best things you can do for your business?

Funnel Your Efforts in the Right Direction

You do the hard work, stress out the same, and risk as much or more than other professionals in your field. Yet they end up generating more revenues than you. How does that happen?

Well, to give it to you straight, you may be missing out on the crucial details that can make or break your business. We often tend to sweep those minutiae under the carpet or overlook them, not understanding how they might serve us.

Here's what you need to do: channel your efforts in the direction where it makes an impact. And how are you going to do that? This is where my book will help you.

This book will be your guide and help you navigate the loopholes and mazes of the fitness and training business. It will teach you how to generate consistent leads and turn reliable prospects into your fitness/health training business.

Every success journey begins with one step taken in the right direction, followed by more steps. It's becoming more and more challenging to thrive in the modern market, considering the increasing competition and variety. Under such conditions, sticking to traditional methods of running a business won't cut it. Modern markets demand that you find new paths, engage with the audience, and remain consistent while you're at it. Your audience can be devoted, a literate brand evangelist, or completely uninformed – it's your job to appeal to them and then to retain them.

My name is Tony Deoleo, and I see myself in you. I am working as a fitness expert and celebrity fitness trainer in the capital of fitness, Los Angeles. Through my experience, research, and extensive travel, I have learned from many masters of the field, both old and new. I have worked with giant revenue-generating firms and some highly successful marketing and sales representatives. Being in one field does not restrict you from seeking more knowledge and experience from other disciplines.

All of the ideas I propose in this book are well-tested, result-oriented, and products of my experience. I might have generated millions in my fitness career, but sometime back, I was just an ordinary guy with dreams of hitting it big. By applying the secrets of success that I am going to share with you, I got a response that blew me away.

I implemented my theories into the lives of hundreds and thousands. I worked with over 30 teams and hundreds of new clients over the past 20 years, to whom I proved these concepts as a key to unlock success. I poured my success potion into their dying fitness business plans and brought them back to their rigorous lifestyles.

By implementing my model, which I based on my knowledge, experience, and skills, I pushed my business in the right direction and watched my income soar ahead of my competition. And that's how I built my international franchise from scratch.

I am going to share my insights with my readers so they can turn things around, too. Read my proposed plan and learn the secrets to make your fitness business thrive. The steps I list here will help you do better in your field during tough competitions without going down the route of bankruptcy or getting worn out by the time you retire.

Be Passionate about Your Profession, and Professional about Your Passion

To reap the maximum output from your passion as well as profession, you need to form a working alliance between the two. This means you need to weld your passion and profession and make sure you do not deviate from the actual pattern, which should be to give your 100 percent to help your clients gain physical and mental stability. To make enough money to reach where you want, you have to discover your full potential.

The world is changing at a rapid pace. And it will be your loss if you do not make the most of it. You don't just need to upgrade your methods of advocating your business, but you also need to invest in yourself – just the way you do with your clients as a fitness trainer! You can make them work together by integrating modern techniques with conventional methods of fitness training. But as a fitness trainer, you need to be visionary enough to predict the future – if not predict, then plan!

Your preparation must begin from the very first phase: correct your business model and the way you lead it. No one doubts your passion, ability, skills, or talent, but in the modern era, the game is all about the mindset – how you pay attention to the little details and work with them!

Being in this field for many years, I have helped thousands of individual trainers and large facilities in retaining potential profits and upgrading their niche. It is imperative for my readers to know I am not just someone selling them fitness business information. Instead, as I said in the beginning, I see myself in my readers, and I'm looking to help them.

I have been where you stand right now. Only, I climbed the right steps at the right time. I am a fitness pro and have owned personal training businesses, established them, and have been consulting for a good part of my life. I have leading results based on personal training for those seeking excellence. Speaking of my own experiences and my 'qualifications,' I have an individualized approach through which I try to balance the best of both worlds – your passion and profession.

I've had the privilege of personally training over 1000 Fitness Professionals and conducting over 40,000 fitness consultations over the past 20 years. I have trained general managers, gym owners, fitness managers, and personal trainers on how to sell their personal training services from the point of sales and fitness consultations. From client training to providing knowledge and practical techniques, I make sure to integrate what I have learned and experienced in my sessions. This helps my clients transform themselves and achieve optimal health naturally.

In my tenure, I have had many clients who had given up on themselves and their goals because of inconsistent efforts (or putting efforts in the wrong direction). But as soon as they aligned their efforts with my guidance and devised plan, the results spoke for themselves! Our website is flooded with clients' feedback and positive testimonies, and celebrity reviews that you can check out for yourself.

I derive personal satisfaction from seeing people working smart rather than hard. A very cliché term in our fitness world is 'go hard or go home.' But if you keep going only hard and not smart, you will probably end up having to wind your business down. With this approach in mind, I am leading my vision to make an impact in the field of health and to influence people's lives positively.

I congratulate you for taking the time out to invest in yourself; this is the best long-term investment that you can make. Pat yourself on the back – you have already won half the battle! You're on your way toward progress and growth. Realization is half the battle won in any situation; all that remains now for you to do is educate yourself to discover your hidden potential and channel it toward achieving your goal.

Throughout this book, I will highlight bona fide methods to bag better deals for your business. I will also talk about how technology can boost your business' market share.

"A goal without a plan is just a wish."

Antoine de Saint-Exupéry

Closing a Deal!

Identifying the right audience through your professional and interpersonal skills is critical in shaping your sales outcome. That's how you can claim a greater market share.

Been there, done that!

I know the hard work and trouble an entrepreneur goes through to establish a high-functioning business module. From my experiences, I can say the biggest hurdle that stands in the way of business growth is the lack of correct knowledge about how you address problems that will inevitably arise. Several other factors contribute to it. When I started, I noticed that too many new trainers began their personal training career with very low chances of succeeding over the years. That's because they cannot close the personal training sales and convert fitness consultations into new clients (meaning new business)!

Although understandably, a fitness client differs from all other clients, you still need to lead with the agenda that every interested person is your potential client. If they have already taken out time from their schedules and visited you to find fitness options, it means they have already stepped into the circle. Now, whether you keep them or lose them depends on how influential and convincing you are for them.

This leads to my real motivation behind writing this book. I realized that as fitness trainers, we are not just training people to get into shape. If you look at it clearly, we are working as operational field doctors, but without the degree! Let me share a very memorable event from my life as a trainer that I'll probably never forget.

I remember helping this lady's husband, who was overweight and was facing severe health issues such as obesity, the threat of cardiovascular diseases, and high blood pressure plus fluctuating sugar levels. They came to me with their problem. As the program ended, I was successfully able to help my client reduce his weight and also improve his health, physical as well as mental. I still remember that woman's face and her words when she said, "You are an angel. You saved my husband's life." That was my moment of realization that I am not just a personal trainer, and neither are you. I am so much more than that!

The incident moved me so much that even today when I think about it, her words resonate with me. I believe as fitness trainers, we have a responsibility that is bigger than just shaping people's physical bodies. We work toward improving people's health and lifestyle by working on both domains, physical and mental.

As fitness trainers, we invest our lives in making others' lives. In this book, I address my readers who're looking to be better in every aspect of their life, professional and personal.

After training and developing thousands of fitness professionals, I noticed a declining graph in the productivity of newcomers. Why are these new businesses shutting down? It is because they are unprepared. It's only logical that failure occurs when you step into something without adequate knowledge and skills.

The root problem is the inability of fitness personnel to use proper processes to run fitness consultations, and turn a prospect into a fitness client. A great fitness trainer is identified by their ability and flexibility. Gym owners are failing because they don't understand how business models operate!

To address this issue and help pros stuck in this loophole, I came up with a perfect three secret steps system that I have used to develop over 30 teams and close 100% of our fitness consultations.

It is always nerve-wracking to head into a closing conversation with a prospect. No matter how solid your presentation was or how impressed the client seemed during the demo, there's always a slight chance of losing a deal. Sometimes the client might be reluctant or hesitant toward the subscription, or they might ask for a price that you cannot deliver. Here, you need to dictate your business features as benefits to the client. This is very crucial in retaining a client while also dealing with customer service. The key is to use the right tips, right words, and right techniques at the right time. In this book, I will tell you how to do that.

I made the three secret steps system available for every one of you to help you achieve great success in your fitness career. This book will guide fitness professionals and gym owners to use the '3 secret steps' system to close 100 percent of their fitness consultations. It will teach them the right process to close all fitness consultations and turn their prospects into personal training clients.

The book will guide trainers to earn big while helping their clients achieve their fitness goals. The goal is to keep a balance! Yes, you can catapult your fitness club to success, and at the same time, enjoy the benefits of a wonderful career. You're a fitness professional, and you save lives through your business. Once you understand that, there will be no stopping you!

Chapter 2
Meet and Greet!

As cliché as it may sound, the first impression leaves the deepest impact. Especially in dealing with clients, you need to be very careful about the way you portray yourself to them. The first session always determines whether it will make or break the deal. Screening and consultation of new clients is critical for fitness trainers. It is one of the foremost to-dos which demand focus as well as planning.

As a personal trainer, once you have worked in the field with people, the screening process becomes second nature. However, as this first session plays an integral part in determining your overall success rate, you need to be mindful of how you execute it. Screening and consultation, if done right, paves the way for subsequent procedures to fall into place.

So, it is imperative to learn how to meet and greet and screen and consult your clients. You have to make sure you don't miss out on any major risk factors because this is what efficient fitness trainers do!

The key to successful training is knowing what questions to ask during the first appointment. I have been in the fitness industry for almost two decades now. I've dedicated a big part of my life to shape not just my clients' bodies but their lives. I understand the delicate nature of training people to help them achieve their desired body goals. I have been where you are right now. The reason I can expound on all the minute details and loopholes is that I have learned from my experiences.

Often, fitness trainers overlook details, only noticing them in hindsight. This can eventually become destructive to their futures.

This chapter focuses on getting your client meetings fixed. Based on my experience, training, and research, I will help you identify major risk factors. These will cue you in on present exercise experience and expectations when working with both current and new clients. This chapter comprises of tips that will help you navigate your clients' queries to the training subscription.

Planning Ahead – The Importance of Planning Coaching Sessions

The preparation to execute a 10/10 meet and greet session starts *before* a prospective client walks through your door, not after it.

To get to know your client, you may put up a basic form on your website or emailing service to schedule an appointment with them. This way, you will have a little background on who you are meeting. You need to show you care about your clients and gain their full attention.

Here's a tip: Use 'Google forms.' They save you both cost and time.

If you have a detailed form as part of appointment scheduling, it might save you from future detailed sessions. However, the problem that may arise with this strategy is that many times people only submit half-filled forms, especially if the forms are too descriptive. So, it is crucial to ask fewer but precise questions. You can collect the rest of the information during a one-on-one conversation.

An important thing to remember, which will help you self-analyze, is that you are not the only one testing your client during the session. The question-answer session goes both ways. Just as you observe the client, they are observing you, too. They notice how interested you are in what they have to say. They see the way you talk, speak, and listen to them.

Listening is the most crucial point of all. To be an effective speaker, you need to be an active listener. Listen to what your clients have to say to you; give them time and space so you can develop a bond over the conversation.

To begin with, you need to make sure the client feels comfortable. Don't over-do it, but make sure your body language conveys that they are sitting with a trusted friend. Ensure your clients that any information they provide is confidential, and anything asked during the screening and greeting will help you improve their experience. Any information that you request from a client will help you in defining a better, customized, and more precise plan for each individual.

Emphasize the importance of sharing information about themselves and their routine, and be honest in your response to their answers. To yield optimum benefits of the training program, the clients must provide complete details–from name and age to what they eat in a day and how much they walk.

Do not just walk unprepared into the room with a client for an introductory meeting, assuming everything will go smoothly. As a fitness professional, it is your job to find out what your clients need – and it's better if you do it in advance. This way, you will know how to plan a personal training session, which will cater to all their needs and help them achieve their body goals. Not everyone wants to lose weight; maybe this person wants to build muscles and put on some mass. You cannot deal with every client in the same way. You need to adjust your methods as per the clients' needs and demands every time.

You may need to ask your clients:

- Do they want to build muscles?
- Are they looking to lose some pounds, or are they just trying to build up stamina?
- Do they want to work on one specific muscle or need to get in shape overall?
- Do they want to just feel better about their bodies?

For whatever reason they walk into your office, you need to identify their goals and sketch the most suitable plan for them. You have to tailor your expertise and approach according to their needs. Once a client is enrolled, take some time to devise a customized plan meeting their requirements, motivation, and health condition.

Also, don't just lay out a workout plan from the very first day. Prepare a collective pathway incorporating complete lifestyle modifications for them to work with, such as food habits and sleeping routine. Get your clients excited about walking down the road to health and fitness with a roadmap in place.

General Client Information

Everything starts with the name. To become familiar with your potential clients, use a detailed form with space for every query.

Following is a general overview of the topics known as general information. These topics are an essential part of the primary questionnaire provided to the clients and help trainers save clients' data.

- Name – well, that's obvious!
- Age – this information is beneficial in determining the intensity of the program that you must design. The pressure a body of an adolescent can work with will not be the same for an older adult.
- Gender – this information is needed for demographic purposes. It also helps trainers devise particular exercises associated with a specific gender (keeping in mind the reps, the weight, and the intensity).
- Sleeping habits – the impact of a good sleeping habit on the overall physique is unparalleled to any other daily routine. Poor sleeping habits are linked to poor recovery habits, which leads to lower growth hormone excretion and more mental fatigue. Sleeping abnormalities can disrupt metabolism as well, which affects your muscle strength and mass gaining.
- Water intake – you need to make sure your clients stay hydrated, during as well as after the session.
- Occupation – this part of the questionnaire, although very confidential for some clients, is an important aspect. It also sets the basis for the upcoming

discussion on money matters. Knowing your clients' occupation also helps you know them better. For instance, what is their lifestyle? How often do they remain seated behind their desk during the day hours?

- Preferred time slot – you must always have flexible options for your clients in order to bag a definite deal. Because of various reasons, some clients may like to work five times a week, while the rest may prefer to work out over the weekends only.
- Body Measurements - this section plays a critical role in helping physical fitness trainers establish the most suitable plan for their clients, according to their distinct body types. Body measurements help to calculate the BMI (Body Mass Index) and other such physical measures.
- Weight – this is where the entire idea of staying fit and healthy revolves. It is a fundamental factor that helps determine your clients' body goals as soon as they walk through your door. Do not just ask your clients their weight, but measure it yourself to be sure about the situation. This helps keep your clients

motivated as they feel the sense of achievement by accomplishing short-term goals.

- Height– based on national height and weight standards, height is a determining factor in setting your clients' goals.
- Body Composition – without a doubt, this is one of the most critical pieces of information at a fitness coach's disposal. Knowing the body composition serves as a reevaluation tool. It helps compare the ratio of body fat to lean muscle. Knowing this ratio is essential to designing suitable exercises with varying repetitions depending on the ratio.

The Health Check

Before you train a new client, you want to be sure about their relevant medical history. Ask questions and note down all the information provided (if it isn't already a part of your questionnaire) regarding previous medical histories such as cardiac diseases, allergies, breathing problems, flat feet, or such. Some questions you may want to put in this section are:

- Do you suffer from regular back problems?

- Have you recently had any surgeries?
- Do your joints create certain unpleasing sensations while performing any exercise?
- Have you ever had a cardiac attack or surgery?
- Have you experienced extreme chest discomfort before?
- Do your ankles swell after running or standing for a while?
- Do you have any breathing problems?
- Do you smoke or drink? If yes, then how often?
- Do you suffer from bronchitis or asthma?

Knowing your clients' medical history is critical for many reasons. First, you get to understand your clients, what they want, and what they expect from you. Second, it helps you tweak the strategy you may have in mind for them. Third, by making suitable adjustments, you can make sure the client does not walk out of your training session in pain, not to return, ever! Remind your clients to inform you at any level when they feel physical pain beyond the expected body discomfort that comes from pushing yourself.

Talk Things Out

Fitness is a long-term plan. Anything that comes fast goes fast. Remind your clients that you are working not just to help them achieve their body goals in a healthy way, but to also maintain the results over longer periods. Do not keep your clients under any misconceptions by promising unrealistic goals. Discuss your training style upfront with your clients, make sure you deliver your best and make it clear that you expect their 100% in response to your efforts.

In this phase of meeting with the clients, you may be asked what type of coach you are. For instance, are you a cheerleader? Or are you a strict type who makes sure people weep their sweat out? Or are you a pusher who always leads their clients to push themselves beyond their apparent limits? Do you emphasize a whole-body approach?

The reason that getting to know your clients is highly emphasized because you are not just collecting information on a piece of paper but shaping someone's future. You, as a fitness trainer, have a responsibility far more significant than just shaping clients' bodies: you shape their lives and the way they perceive life. Talking to your clients will help you smooth out things while planning for their 'new chosen lifestyle.'

Below are some points that you should go through with your clients to get an insight into how you must treat each one of them:

- Stress Level: ‘Are you easily frustrated?’ ‘Do you feel under a lot of stress at work?’ ‘Do you enjoy an active social life?’ These related questions are linked and help you know your clients better. For instance, if they have trouble sleeping, you might recommend that they restrict their intake of caffeine 4 to 6 hours before bed and provide some extra supplements to help boost their health.
- Long and short-term goals: If the client is new to a workout routine, they may have unrealistic expectations from the fitness program. Don’t make any assumptions, and listen to them carefully as they explain what they have in mind. Once you get a clear picture, you can help them set realistic deadlines and goals, both short-term and long-term. If their expectations are practical, they won’t lose hope, nor will they run out of motivation after just a week or two of training.

- Eating Habits: ask clients about their daily eating habits and notice if there's a pattern. Maybe they are excessively consuming one kind of nutrient, and that is overshadowing the overall 'balanced diet' they must take. Combine a series of health tips to help your clients achieve their body goals by staying on the right track. Eating and exercise go hand in hand. Though the body is shaped in the gym, it is maintained inside the kitchen. As a fitness trainer, you must know your clients' eating habits so you can fix them if needed.
- Any Recent Exercise Program: you must ask your clients about recent health sessions they might have attended or the last health routine they were following. Take note of what they have been doing and determine what they *should have been* doing instead. This way, you can mold your fitness plan for them accordingly. Even if the clients haven't been doing any resistance exercise, in particular, this information will help you get them started based on their previous routine.

Balancing Your Personal and Professional Relationship

Although you want your first impression to be friendly, you should never compromise on professionalism. After all, you are their trainer; they have to follow your instructions to achieve optimum health benefits!

You not only want to impress your clients with your knowledge on health and your fitness skills but also want to deliver information in a professional environment. This aspect may go overlooked while designing a personal fitness program, but it has significant legal and ethical implications. Keep the following tips in mind:

- Never yell at your clients, no matter how frustrating the situation may become.
- Be a friend, not their best friend. You still want them to listen to your advice when it comes to health, so don't be too easygoing.
- Don't be unnecessarily rude to your clients.
- Appreciate them and encourage their efforts.

If you compromise on maintaining professional boundaries, you might unintentionally end up making fitness sessions uncomfortable for both, so much so that they may not want to return for further sessions. Always ensure to make your clients feel welcome. For some people, it is already a big challenge to step out of their comfort zones. Your job as a fitness trainer is to let your clients know that you welcome them and will help them achieve their goals. Even something as simple as a smile can have a powerful impact on your clients' moods and motivations!

Here is a 3-page form that you may print and present to your clients:

WELCOME WORKOUT

[illegible]

Chapter 3
S.E.E

"Human behavior flows from three main sources: Desire, Emotion, and Knowledge."

-Plato

Emotions are an essential part of the human psyche. They add meaning to everyday tasks. A life without emotions is like a book of black and white pictures. You can feed the stray animals, spend time with your family, achieve good grades, and ace a presentation – but what would they mean without emotions?

From excitement to resentment, sorrow to happiness, satisfaction to disappointment – emotions add texture to human lives. They shape your cognitive patterns, actions, and behaviors. Your emotions also influence your decisions.

However, to understand the emotions you experience, you must equip yourself with better tools to identify and control them. Once you've learned the art of controlling your emotions, you can execute your success plans. Learn to take control of your mind – that is the most powerful tool!

To define your emotions, you must understand them first. The three critical components of emotions are:

- Subjective component (the way you experience emotions)
- Physiological component (the way your body reacts to emotions)
- Expressive component (the way you act according to your emotions)

All these elements play distinctive roles in regulating your emotional responses. The emotions you feel can be quick or long-lasting. No matter how much you suppress them, your emotions will seep out, one way or the other.

If I feel nervous at the start of a meeting, and I keep fearing and doubting my abilities, I will end up with an enclosed consultation. Before addressing an audience, I need to feel what's going on within me. I can change the lives of my clients, but I need to be in control of myself for that to happen. If I keep telling myself that I will fail, my thoughts will take on a similar shape, and failure will be my fate. You must have read about the power of positive thoughts and how they impact your mood, mind, and life. Negative thoughts have the same effect. The consequences are far-reaching and impact your physical, mental, emotional, and even social health. Also, they impact your personal and professional life.

But can you shape your emotions and their strength to serve you?

Can you channel your emotions to achieve your biggest life goals?

To clear any contradictions, while you are advised to avoid it, negativity is a part of life. It is inevitable, but if not controlled, it can derail your life. It may also stunt your personal and professional growth.

What if I told you that you could shape your emotions and their strength to serve you? What if I told you that you could channel your emotions to achieve your biggest life goals?

It is okay to be negatively affected by your emotions. It's understandable if a person dwells in a negative mental space occasionally; sometimes, it even helps in evaluating your life decisions. However, it is unhealthy to remain in that mental and emotional space for long. Negativity can be a choice. When you constantly think you will fail, the fact is, you will. In contrast, if you channel your thoughts in a positive direction, you put yourself in a much better place, physically and mentally, whether you succeed or not.

A fitness trainer plays a role beyond getting their clients in shape. In your daily routine, you are surrounded by different people. You cannot expect all of them to share the same mindset and perception as you. You can help others around you transform their negative thinking into positive by strengthening their conduct.

Take out a few seconds and think of the emotions you have experienced in the past few days. Try listing all the emotions you have ever felt your entire life. You are in for a quick self-analysis exercise.

What's on that list? I'm assuming you have included emotions like anger, happiness, gratefulness, sadness, fear, confusion, stress, pride, and amazement, etc.

Now, put your emotions into two categories – positive and negative emotions.

Feeling positive or negative is natural. What you have to do is learn to deal with stress. Medical research has coined a term called 'positive stress'– what does it mean? We have always heard that stress is bad for us, so how come it is healthy all of a sudden? Well, we might have labeled all the difficult emotions as 'negative,' but that does not make them bad. What matters is how you use your emotions as steps to achieve your goals – in this case, to achieve your fitness goals. You have to be motivated and determined. Your emotions are the best determinant of your performance and the best motivators you can use.

If you analyze your behavior, you will realize it is heavily influenced by how you think, perceive, and communicate. All of these form our beliefs. Belief is having faith in yourself and your abilities. Belief is about being determined about your goals. Your belief system is a driving force of your behavior.

When we have a strong belief in specific ideologies or when we are determined about something emotionally, we tend to consciously and unconsciously look for proof and experiences that will reinforce them. Our emotions are fuel for the reality that creates our worldview.

So how can you shape your negative emotions to achieve your desired fitness goals?

Negative emotions generate a sense of threat or a response that warns you about the challenges that you may need to deal with. For instance, fear, a negative emotion, can drive you to protect yourself from possible threats. Anger can warn you that someone's breaching your boundaries. Anger is a signal that may show you need to act. It can build your stamina to endure more rounds and bear more strength training.

You can use emotions like anger inside the gym environment. However, some people ought to implement positive emotions, which are also equally healthy and beneficial to attain their desired body goals. Positive emotions increase your attention, memory, and awareness. They enable you to take in more information and understand how crosscutting disciplinary ideas interrelate.

Positive emotions expose us to the new world of opportunities, helping us learn more and build our skills. This helps us achieve better results–in terms of quantity and quality. Emotions can help us achieve our fitness goals by aligning them with our workout routines, enhancing our performance and productivity to perform tasks better and more efficiently.

This leads us to the subject of how emotions and experiences are shaped by S.E.E (Significant Emotional Experience). What is SEEs? Let me tell you. Our emotions tell us a million things in a million different ways. Whether they incline us to express, hide, or suppress, they drive our reactions, behaviors, and thoughts to an extent we do not even realize.

Significant Emotional Experiences define us. SEEs are who we are and who we have the potential to become. We encounter SEEs continually, and looking at them is like looking at our life's timeline. These SEEs and our responses shape us as humans. They change our perceptions, actions, and outlook about progress. How we address, encounter, and deal with our personal SEEs influences how we react to situations in life.

As a fitness trainer, it is one of your vital duties to identify your clients' emotions and to get to know their 'WHY' – their reason behind joining the fitness club. To bag the optimum fitness experience for your clients, you need to know their SEEs. You are dealing with humans, and they are all different from one another. So you need to deal with them in ways tailored to their needs.

Motivation is one of the core elements that make any process happen. Without motivation, a task becomes mechanical, involving no feelings or passion. Motivation is driven by passion and will; it is what your client feels as they walk through your gym's door. They have a vision, a goal, and a deep desire for what they want to achieve. As a fitness trainer, you need to develop a bond with your clients that will help you understand them better. You need to know the 'why' behind their will.

What gets you out of bed every morning? What makes you drag your tired body out of bed on a cold winter morning to perform your routine tasks? Is it the alarm clock or the dog licking your face? What's the real motivation behind you leaving your comfort and going out in the world?

Most people think adopting a healthy lifestyle is the most difficult change in their lives. When it comes to implementing bold life changes, there is no bigger change than having a baby. Yet most people out there want to have them – and not just once but multiple times. A similar example is smoking. Hardly anyone enjoys their first cigarette, and yet people end up becoming chain-smokers – why?

Do you see the pattern here? What's the common denominator of these two different experiences?

It is emotions!

People have babies as the emotional reward of being a parent outweighs the challenges. People become smokers because the rewards of being associated with a particular social group or activity offset the downsides.

Emotions fuel motivation. They are the secret weapons to life-changing steps that change your habits, and thus lifestyles, such as having a healthy eating habit or exercise routine.

The early path of fitness is hard for everyone—no one's born with the ideal physique. In fact, the way we understand fitness keeps changing as we grow up. A fitness routine for a 20-year-old will definitely vary from a 40-year-old's.

It takes some time for people to get comfortable with their fitness routine. Why did I quit my job to run a fitness business? Why, out of all the choices I could make, did I choose this path? Why was I 'motivated' to become fit and healthy? These are all self-assessment questions that you need to ask your clients to address their goals, routines, and fitness routine. Get to know the powerful, emotional 'why' that works as a motivational factor behind their decision to join the gym.

Having a personal session with your client about their fitness routine and 'why' they want to be fit can have multiple benefits. Let's call understanding your client's 'why' before the 'how' of training them as emotional relevance of exercise.

To achieve optimum results from your workout routine and consultations, you need to know the emotional connection people have with their body and weight. Sometimes people don't achieve their desired results because they are not sure about what drives their passion for coming to the gym every day. Even people who are deeply emotional about their weight are not seeking weight loss directly. They are really seeking the way they will feel when they are fitter. It just so happens they will most likely also be lighter or leaner.

An emotional session can help you build a connection and a rapport with your clients. Exploring their relevant information enables you to establish a bond with them. It lets you connect with their stories and life and get to know the powerful emotional drivers that motivate them to do anything in life.

Find out what your client values the most in their life. What will become instantly better in your clients' lives when they get fit? What will they get from getting in shape? Once you find answers to these links, you can measure their progress and frame it in terms of how fitness will play a part in enhancing these goals.

If you don't make efforts to get to know your clients, you are just another personal fitness trainer who only knows how to demonstrate push-ups and squats. You are not just selling the program; you are putting a piece of yourself in every client you consult!

We all have something so powerful inside each one of us that can motivate us to live a healthier life. Find that motivational trigger to help your clients achieve bigger and better goals!

Chapter 4
Fitness Prescription

Exercise prescriptions play an important role in shaping overall fitness, especially for clients and trainers who seek optimum health regime. One of the many things that fitness trainers – good fitness trainers, to be specific – do is keep a progress record of their clients.

To do that, they need records for when the client first enrolls in the program until the very recent evaluation. For this, sometimes sports physicians and personal trainers develop 'exercise prescriptions' based on factors that influence each client's specific fitness plan.

Besides many others, the two top reasons to get exercise prescriptions are efficiency and safety. An exercise plan is very critical, and it needs to be designed, keeping in mind all the technicalities, restrictions, strengths, and weaknesses of the client.

Since we are dealing with humans and not machines, we cannot run every plan with the same script. Each client's needs and 'case study' varies from the other. Thus, a fitness trainer needs to be vigilant while designing a specific plan for the client's goals, health status, interests, and abilities.

Whether it's for yourself or your client, keeping track of progress is imperative to accomplishing fitness goals. Some reasons why keeping a progress report is so important are:

- It indicates clients' performances
- It can help trainers hold their clients accountable
- It is a great motivational tool
- It helps to keep clients' goals at the forefront of your mind

Before getting your clients on track (starting a physical activity program), you might want to perform a screening test. The screening test session can be held before the first training class or with the meet and greet session (as discussed in chapter 2).

FITNESS PRESCRIPTION

[illegible]

Screening tests help bring out any medical history or sensitivities a client may have. Also, it may help mitigate any adverse reaction to the advised exercise that the client may demonstrate. This is important because even the slightest change in physical activity can trigger chemical changes that are reflected in overall health patterns.

Some signs and symptoms that are linked to high-risk include:

- Shortness of breath at rest or with mild exertion
- Orthopnea

- Pain or any kind of discomfort (pressure) in chest, arms, jaw, neck or any other areas that could be due to ischemia
- Dizziness
- Palpitations
- Intermittent claudication
- Ankle oedema
- Tachycardia
- Any known heart murmuring patterns
- Unusual fatigue

This information helps fitness trainers evaluate their decisions regarding medical clearance for their clients before further testing.

Elements of an Exercise Prescription

Although customizable, there are some key factors, known as general exercise prescriptions. The factors mentioned below contain information that can be fetched from the primary questionnaire handed out to the clients during the time of enrollment (refer to chapter 2). These prescriptions take into consideration conditioning principles, which may include the following:

Physical Examination or Health Status Questionnaire

The client is handed a general questionnaire that determines any major health issues that they may have. This also includes a section for mentioning any allergies that can be triggered by any food items, considering many personal trainers work on optimal health plan and nutritional intake for their clients as well, advising them about what to eat, add, subtract, increase or reduce from the diet. Most physical trainers require a physician's clearance before they plan a fitness program for their client.

Fitness Assessment and Evaluation

Fitness assessment sets the basis for designing any fitness program. It establishes a baseline for the current fitness status and helps determine the parameters for what sort of exercise you will need to perform. These assessments may include:

- Body composition
- Cardiovascular endurance
- Flexibility
- Blood pressure
- Heart rate

- Strength
- Goals and interests
- Exercise history

These assessments are often repeated after certain intervals to determine the client's progress as well.

Exercise Type

A major part of a fitness prescription is centered on the type of exercises that need to be done. The key to a good fitness prescription is a balance of different exercise routines to help build base fitness, core strength, endurance, stamina, and flexibility. Often, the exercise type varies for the clients, even in the same program, depending on their goal. For instance, running a marathon, trying to get in shape, going to a ski vacation, lowering blood cholesterol, etc.

Cardiovascular Fitness

One of the best ways of regulating blood circulation and increase blood flow for a longer time is by using large muscle groups to perform rhythmic movements. Exercise such as swimming, bicycling, or walking improves the heart's functionality and enhances overall cardiovascular health.

Strength Training

Strength training is one area that varies greatly from person to person due to several factors, i.e., current health status, goals, time duration, stamina, strength, diseases (if any), restrictions, daily routine, etc.

A good fitness prescription includes a mix of all the major muscle movements – involvement of big muscle groups through various combinations. These combinations can be derived through various workings such as against resistance and building strength and balance.

Frequency of Exercises

The crux of exercise prescription lies in ensuring the health and safety of a client. Thus, the 'frequency of exercise' is one such point that ensures clients' health and safety by keeping track of repeated exercise patterns. How often a client exercises, or more importantly, how often a client needs to exercise, marks an important aspect of fitness in making safe progress.

Exercise Duration

Basing on the client's current health status, level of fitness, and past health and fitness history, the exercise prescription varies time duration for each exercise and each set. This is to ensure a smooth start with steady progress. Also, the frequency of exercise and duration are very interchangeable aspects.

Exercise Intensity

One of the most crucial elements of a balanced, efficient, fun, and safe program is the intensity of your exercise. Since every person's body responds differently to the type of exercise and its intensity, this aspect also judges the trainer's ability and skillfulness. Finding the right balance between rest and pushing hard is very critical.

Heart rate measurement is the basic element that is used here to instill any changes in the planning. The intensity of exercise takes into account the body readings. While the client exercises, a fitness trainer may notice their heart rate patterns.

Exercise Session Order

Depending on the client's training goals, this order is amended with time. However, all programs begin with a warm-up and end with a cool down and stretching session.

Exercise Progression

Two-way feedback plays an integral role in marking the daily progress of the client, as well as of the trainer. It is one-way trainers keep their clients on track.

Most trainers keep a chart or table, or before/after pictures and logs to maintain a record of their clients' progress. These notes contain information related to the distance, time, weight, workout, sets, reps, workout type, and how you felt.

Modification of the Exercise

One of the qualities of a standout fitness prescription is that it is flexible and easily adaptable. A client's fitness prescription may require timely changes while still progressing towards their goal. These adjustments are made based on your progress and any uncertain unease that may arise.

However, making modifications in the exercise plan is essential as you need to put your body through different challenges and not just adhere to one routine. Try new types of workouts, take breaks, try new activities, increase or reduce your time of exercise and or play with intensity occasionally.

For the clients, it is wise to visit their physicians now and then to keep them in the loop of the changes in life due to fitness routine.

But Why Do We Need Exercise Prescription?

If you and your client believe in optimum health fitness, then you must be serious about your workout routine. However, the concept of exercise prescription is not just limited to athletes or professional gym buffs. Exercise prescriptions are essential for regular clients as well to keep their body fit and in shape, while making sure the switch in lifestyle caused by new exercise patterns do not cause any negative bodily stresses. A personalized fitness regimen is beneficial as it addresses each client's needs, leading to a healthier lifestyle and recovery.

The body functions efficiently with just the right set of workout routines mentioned in the exercise prescription. The exercise prescription, however, should ensure the inclusion of different lifestyle measures such as goals, daily routine, working hours, physical activity, and the clients' interest.

Body Composition and Important Measurements

As we discussed the importance of keeping track of the clients' progress, one of the simpler ways of doing so is through keeping structured progress reports. This is an effective means of helping clients evaluate their progress and achieve their goals. This report's input can be periodic, depending on the set intervals, including accomplishments, suggestions, and insights, let's say, for the next six weeks.

Body measurements are an effective way of marking the client's progress, especially if their goals are muscle gain or weight loss/fat loss. One can easily track their client's progress with body measurements. This may include the measurement of different body parts such as arms, hips, shoulders, waist, and chest.

In addition, you also check the client's weight along with the body fat percentage. A client might weigh the same as they did at the beginning of the program, but now their weight constitutes of lean muscle and not the fat product, which is a win-win situation and an indicator of health progress.

Some clients are not satisfied if their weight readings are found to be the same, especially if their goals are to either gain muscle mass or lose body fat. In such cases, you must remind them about the difference in body weight contributed by fat and lean muscle.

Weight measurement tests help trainers figure out how much fat needs to be gone from the client's total weight. First, the total body weight test is done, which is followed by a lean body weight test. By simply subtracting the lean body weight from the gross body weight, you get the approximate figure of fat weight that is burned through the workouts.

Another such measure accountable is designing a fitness/exercise prescription is the BMI (Body Mass Index). It is a measure of body fat based on your weight and height. The results from the tests of BMI qualify a person into four basic categories which are healthy, unhealthy, underweight, and overweight. However, the BMI measurements are more of a general guideline rather than the dictation of what a person should weigh.

Once you determine the score of your BMI, you can easily see where you fall:

- 18.5 Or below falls in *Underweight* category
- 18.5 to 24.9 is what is considered as *Normal*
- From 25.0 to 29.9 states *Overweight*
- Point 30 or above is considered *Obese*

Body Fat Percentage

BMI, however, uses the total weight into its evaluation, but unfortunately does not take into account if the calculated weight comes from the lean muscle tissue or the body fat. For instance, if you were to weigh an athlete, contrary to the general belief, you will find their body weight measurements unmatched to their fitness frame. This is because the size is not the only determining factor of body weight; usually, muscle mass weighs more than the fat.

For specific individuals, they might have a high BMI reading but not necessarily a high body fat percentage. Body fat percentage is the total percentage of fat in the human body. This percentage value varies from males to females to be deemed fit, fat, healthy, obese, etc.

Body fat percentages for Females

- 10 – 12 % is considered Essential Fat
- 14 – 20 % is Athletic
- 21 – 24 % is referred to as Fit
- 25 – 31 % is taken as Acceptable Fat
- However, 32 % and above is considered obese

Body Fat Percentages for Males

- 2 – 4 % is considered Essential Fat
- 6 – 13 % is Athletic
- 14 – 17 % is referred to as Fit
- 18 – 25 % is taken as Acceptable Fat
- However, 26 % and above is considered obese

There are several ways to measure a person's body fat percentage. Typically, tools such as skin calipers, a Tanita machine (a bioelectric impedance), Bod Pod, and underwater or hydrostatic weighing techniques are used. Amongst all, the bod pod is considered to be the most accurate and closest to precision by fitness experts. It is also the most preferred method by individuals leading the mission of fat reduction and track progress. The Body Pod or also known as Bod Pod measures body mass by precise scale and volume by the person sitting inside the pod.

A big part of personal training is to ensure the client's progress. To do so, tracking progress plays an integral part in any personal fitness trainer/consultant. Report tracks ensure that the program is working out for the clients, and they are meeting their fitness goals.

The factors mentioned above are all accountable and should be addressed with the responsibility they demand. They should be modified according to timely recordings found after every interval of track reporting of the client's health progress, and how far their bodies are responsive to the program, they are on. Fitness training is a team sport that requires an equal amount of effort from the client, as well as the trainer. It requires you and your clients to get involved and put forth their best efforts to achieve success.

Fortunately, for the personal trainer, these steps in the screening and assessment processes are step-by-step laid out for you with very little guess-work involved.

We emphasized the screening process and the primary session of meet and greet in the previous chapters. You can get to the heart of what you want to achieve and why you started training in the first place by making your fitness regime more productive. A fitness prescription plays an integral part in designing a distinctive program that will get your client's results. The same steps can be used to reassess and reevaluate to prove how successful the exercise program has been as the clients make strides to their goals.

Chapter 5
Welcome Workout Assessment

Stretching

Exercise even before exercise – that's stretching for you. Stretching makes up for an important part of your whole fitness routine. When it comes to 'pre-workout sessions,' stretching helps your muscles to relax and your body to become more pliable. This decreases risks of any possible injury due to any sudden pressure on the already tensed muscle and muscle fibers. In addition to overall body stretching, you may want to especially target those muscles and body parts that you are going to use in the latter exercise. In order to help prevent injury and execute a safe workout routine, you need to remember these points in your pre and post-workout stretch sessions:

- Do not stretch too far, especially if you are new to workouts. Assuming that most of the clients standing with us for the welcome workout session might have little to no prior experience of professional workout training, you need to make sure they don't overdo. After all, it's just a pre-assessment exercise. Just get a slight stretch and try to hold the posture for 10 seconds or as guided by the fitness trainer

- Try to hold the posture in a comfortable position. If your body is not at rest or in comfort while stretching, your body tension might divert and will cause cramps in other muscles. The stretch session should subside as you hold it.
- Keep breathing during and after the sets/reps. Breathe slowly and exhale as you bend forward.
- Stretch and hold, do not bounce, as bouncing tightens the muscle further
- Don't try to be flexible – don't rush your body movement into bearing tensile pressure. It's just a pre-workout assessment habit. Just learn to stretch properly, and surely flexibility will come with time.

Additional benefits of stretching are:

- Increases range of motions
- Helps to coordinate by allowing freer and easier movements

- Reduces muscle tension
- Makes your body feel relaxed
- Prevents injuries such as muscle strains. (A strong pre-stretched muscle resists stress better than a strong unstretched muscle.)
- Stretching helps prepare the body for workout sessions ahead. It signals the body to embrace and relax, so that in case of any pressured movements, the body does not take it as a surprise against its general nature
- Promotes circulation
- Develops body awareness
- Improves flexibility

Hip Flexors

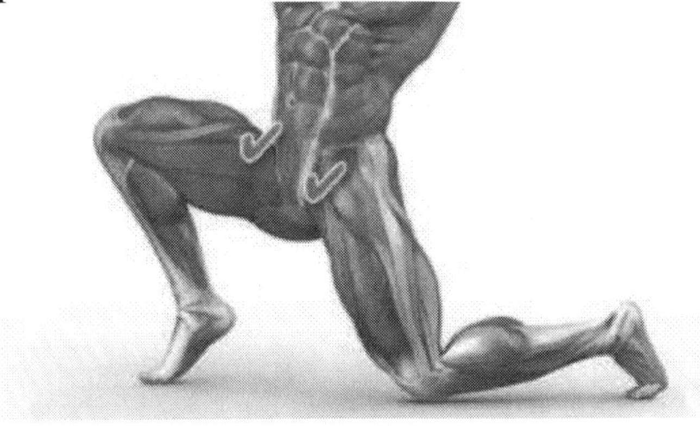

Your hip flexors are a muscle group near the top of your thighs. Hip flexors play a key part in making your lower body move. They let your body (lower body especially) to bend, walk, kick, and swivel the hips. However, if you perform any sudden movement or perform any exercises without stretching, you put your hip flexors at risk of stretching or tearing.

The mild tearing of the hip flexor strain can cause discomfort and could even lead to bigger problems such as having muscle spasms or general muscle pain.

Why we reinforce to perform hip flexors before the welcome workout assessment is to avoid any probable injury and that too on the very first day of the rest of the plan. Tight hip flexors can also make it difficult for the glutes to activate. It is due to the fact that they are opposing muscle groups, and when one of them is tight, it causes the other one to lengthen. And when a muscle is more lengthened than its general capacity, it takes away some of its ability to contract. When your glutes are in this compromised position, it can cause other muscles to do more work than they should, making your workouts less efficient and sometimes increasing your risk of injury. Pair the hip flexor stretch with foam roller assessment exercises.

Lunging Hip Flexor Stretch – stretching for hips, quads, and glutes

https://www.acefitness.org/education-and-resources/lifestyle/exercise-library/142/kneeling-hip-flexor-stretch/

- Kneel on your left knee

- Lace your right foot flat on the floor in front of you and do a knee bent
- Lean forward, stretching the left hip towards the floor
- Squeeze the butt (squeezing or clenching your butt a little will allow you to stretch your hip flexor even more)
- Hold for 10 seconds and perform several reps as guided by your fitness trainer
- Switch sides and repeat

As a fitness trainer, it is fantastic to see your clients' progress! You have the opportunity of helping your clients reach their goals; you watch them change their lifestyle, habits, and above all, their mindsets. However, a fundamental part of an effective "mentorship" is assessment.

Once you have signed a client, an integral part of starting a dedicated plan is pre-assessment. This chapter includes details and guidance about testing your clients' fitness level by assessing their flexibility, endurance, upper and lower body strength, mobility, cardiovascular endurance, and reaction, etc. So let's dive in! As discussed earlier, after the meet and greet, the client has to fill a questionnaire. This form is a detailed fill-in-the-blank query-based document that prompts information about their current routine, previous habits, exercises, lifestyle, general body description, information about injuries, etc. To begin with, you will walk your clients through a basic structure of what they will be tested for and how their performance will be assessed. Before you even begin, make sure your client understands that this is not a 'challenge' but a healthy workout, which will help you (the fitness trainer) assess their abilities and capacities.

I have carefully devised this multi-step sequential process that will guide fitness consultants to assess their clients and help them better to achieve their fitness goals. You may tweak the process, depending on your circumstances. However, have a basic fitness test template ready for your clients. It is also essential to adapt parts of the test to suit the client, depending on their goals and needs.

As a personal fitness trainer, this test is a great way to set a benchmark by assessing your clients and monitoring their progress – that is, how they improve in the future once they are good to go for the plan. It will also convey your care to your clients; they will know that you have invested in their improvement, as well as encouraged them to perform even better on positive results.

For instance, when your clients notice themselves being able to hold the plank position for a longer period than before, they will feel a sense of pleasure and satisfaction. There is no better motivator than one's own self! If they see they can plank much longer or lift heavier weights or even correct their form better than a month or a week ago, it'll boost their morale. They will work harder and have more faith in you.

The welcome workout is essential as it will provide trainers with an individual fitness profile of their clients. However, make sure you record these test readings as they will be helpful for future result comparisons.

It is important to be aware of the fact that all of your clients' results are going to vary from each other depending on several factors such as their age, gender, body types, current health and fitness level, external factors, etc. These results will help serve you as a guide for future client progress.

Below is a chart you can use to assess your client's progress:

Welcome Workout Assessment

Member Name:		Date:	

Goals:	

Overhead Squat Assessment	Notes	

Warm Up				
Foam Roll				
Stretch				
Dynamic Warm-Up				

Workout Assessment						
Exercise Type	Exercise	Reps	Sets	Weight	Tempo	Notes
Upper Body						
Lower Body						
Core						

Progress Assessment						
Exercise Type	Exercise	Reps	Sets	Weight	Tempo	Notes
Upper Body						
Lower Body						
Core						

Cool Down	
Notes	

What Is Welcome Workout or Fitness Testing Anyway?

A welcome workout is a basic template for assessing the client's core fitness level, capability, strength, and where they stand currently. To give a more 'practical' definition, it is simply taking body measurements and readings in response to different exercises. These results then help determine the type of plan most suitable for the client, keeping into account their results, goals, and motivation level. Examples of fitness testing include taking body measurements such as body composition, girth measurement, checking for any possible disease that may or may not affect the way your fitness plan pans out to be, blood pressure level, body fat percentage, etc.

Why is there a need for fitness test clients' personal training? The three main reasons are:

- Training focus – what are the client's goals and training targets?
- Client Safety – ensuring you don't take your client over their medial limits with the type of training offered.

- Motivation – regular feedback ensures effective communication and brings out positive and better results.

Before starting a program, clients must share their medical history with the personal trainer and also get necessary approvals from their general physician (if required) to proceed with the plan.

Don't be too invasive when asking clients about their injuries. Most of the time, clients may have had an injury in the past, which they have genuinely forgotten about, as it might not have been a pressing issue. However, it is always a wise option to stay cautious.

Most fitness trainers will use more than one type of screening tools and tests to determine their clients' baseline health and fitness. This may include obtaining vital information such as the client's weight, height, resting blood pressure, heart rate, etc.

In addition, the clients may be asked to fill out a questionnaire that requests information regarding their general health. Among many questions, some general ones ask if the client is on any medication, if they have any type of allergies or experience dizziness, and if they have any physical injury that may impair their ability to exercise.

The next step is to take body composition inputs in our assessment, such as BMI (Body Mass Index), fat percentage, and total body weight, including bones, muscles, and fat. The most common methods to take body composition measurements are through BMI, Skinfold Measurements, and BIA (Bioelectrical Impedance Analysis). This is discussed in detail in the next chapter.

Then, the next step calls for some action – it's time to take the floor! Explain to your client what they will be doing on the floor. Again, tell them it's not a challenge; don't rush or go beyond their endurance limit. The test is basically to assess their strength, endurance, and weakness – their capabilities and limitations. Any reading taken during the welcome workout assessment will help fitness trainers create a more suitable plan for the client while keeping in mind all the details regarding their health and body.

As your client takes the floor, your goal is to assess their fitness level. Look out for their strengths and weaknesses. Notice their form and motor chain patterns to analyze their mobility better. This is also an opportunity for the trainer to build a rapport with the client by getting to know them on an emotional level. Try building a bond with them.

As already in the previous chapter, as a fitness trainer, it is one of your vital duties to identify your clients' emotions and to get to know their 'WHY' – their reason behind joining the fitness club. To ensure the optimum fitness experience for your clients, you need to know their SEEs. You are dealing with humans, and they are all different from one another. So you need to deal with them in ways tailored to their needs.

Motivation is one core element that makes any process happen. Without motivation, a task becomes mechanical, devoid of any feelings or passion. Motivation is driven by passion and will; it is what your client feels as they walk through your gym's door. They have a vision, a goal, and a deep desire for what they want to achieve. As a fitness trainer, you need to develop a bond with your clients that will help you understand them better. You need to know the 'why' behind their will.

An essential part of the assessment is cardiovascular endurance testing, which is also known as stress testing. Cardiovascular endurance is a measure of your lungs and heart's work to smoothly regulate the supply of oxygen and energy throughout the body when under physical pressure (during any physical activity or exercise). Several exercises can be used to test for cardiovascular endurance; I have mentioned some below. However, one common way of assessing stress training is by performing on a treadmill or stationary bike. The heart rate and any other significantly changed patterns can be monitored through an attached peripheral device.

Strength testing: It is the measure of maximal stress or force that can be applied at one time by a muscle group. As a general practice, push-ups can be used to test for core strength and stability. However, there are other exercises as well, such as the plank, overhead squats, kettlebell swing, etc. Strength and endurance tests will help trainers pinpoint which muscle groups are stronger, which are vulnerable, and which of them require more attention.

Measuring Flexibility: Flexibility measures are an important element of the welcome workout assessment. They help determine if the client has any postural imbalances, limitations regarding the range of motions or foot instability. There are numerous ways to test for flexibility, such as:

- Sit and reach testing
- Shoulder flexibility testing
- Trunk lift testing

Overhead Squats Assessment

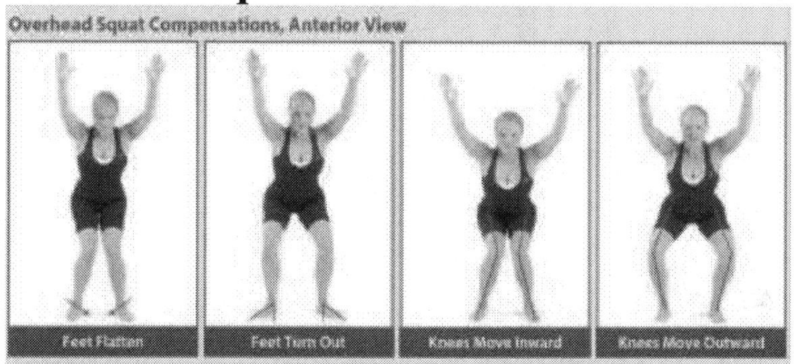

https://www.thefitnesstraineracademy.org/blog/the-overhead-squat-assessment/

Overhead Squat assessment or OHSA is an amazing way of measuring how healthy your clients' kinetic chain is. Before you begin any of these assessments, take real-time feedback from your clients, and ask them how they feel. You need to observe their expressions. Sometimes the client may not say it out of embarrassment or adrenaline, but they overestimate themselves – especially in the first session or welcome workout session. Observe the expressions of your clients and then proceed accordingly.

We use the OHSA to find out the muscle imbalances and possible muscle tightness. We are not required to use the rate of perceived exertion when it comes to OHSA.

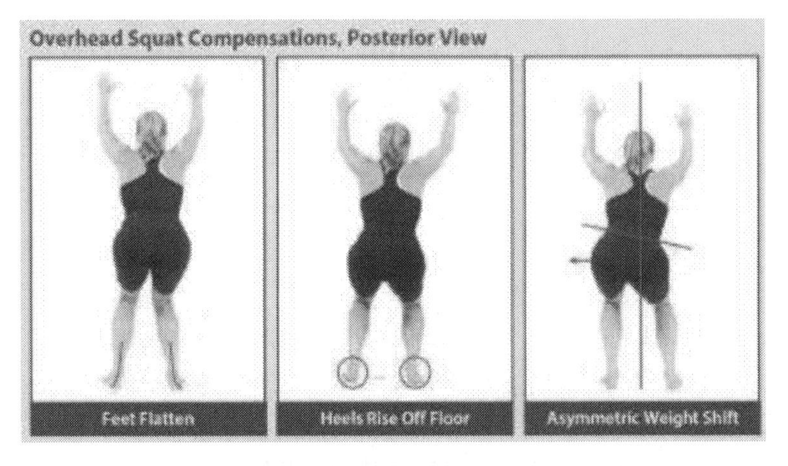

https://www.thefitnesstraineracademy.org/blog/the-overhead-squat-assessment/

Overhead Squat Assessment enables trainers to analyze every part of the kinetic chain for proper function. It is a perfect movement to measure overall musculoskeletal function as it puts in action all musculature from head to toe. To perform an overhead squat assessment:

- Ask your clients to remove their shoes (it's done better without shoes on).

- Tell them to face you with their feet shoulder-width apart and instruct them to raiser their arms over their heads, directing their palms forward.
- Ask them to perform a squat slowly and maintain the position by pausing at the bottom at a certain angle.
- Ask them to repeat while maintaining the posture.
- Repeat the process to ensure that you are noticing the

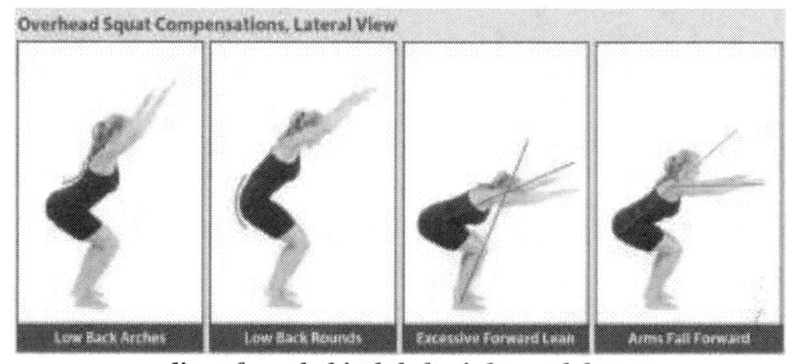

client from behind, left, right, and front.

https://www.thefitnesstraineracademy.org/blog/the-overhead-squat-assessment/

If you suspect the client is not performing well because of the unfamiliarity with the movements, coach them to fix their posture and then retake the readings. Once done, ask your clients how they feel on a scale of 1 to 10. Then repeat the exercise accordingly or move to the next exercise, which is battle ropes.

Foam Roller Assessment

http://www.gippslandstorm.com.au/inspire-foam-roller-exercises.html

After the OHSA, lay a yoga mat and proceed to the next step of assessment – the foam roller. Foam rollers are very effective in releasing muscle knots or trigger points. Foam rollers are tools that target specific areas and help trainers assess if the client has any difficulty in performing certain movements.

In physiology, the term "Myofascial Adhesions" refers to those inflexible or tightened muscles that can be caused by injuries or muscle imbalances. Most of the time, clients do not remember if they have any past injury; it may not even be a problem for them anymore because of their casual routine. However, since foam roller movements lay a certain amount of pressure on targeted muscles, the client may feel slight discomfort in movement, which will tell the trainer which part they need to focus more on and what kind of pain certain exercise movements can cause to the clients.

For the initial assessment, go for the moderate intensity of the foam roller – not too light to be undetectable or not too hard to cause unnecessary discomfort. Generally, you're looking for that "it hurts so good" level of discomfort. To carry out a foam roller assessment, follow these steps, and then proceed to the next step of assessment:

- Target a muscle – especially if the client tells you they have any sore muscles
- Control your body as you slowly lower the targeted area, so it's centered above the roller.
- Lower your body on the foam roller
- Make sure not to go beyond the discomfort point, but to just hit it
- Hold it on for 20 to 30 seconds
- By going back and forth, you can further stimulate the area

- Continue to move slowly along the muscle with the roller, stopping and holding in the areas that need more focus.

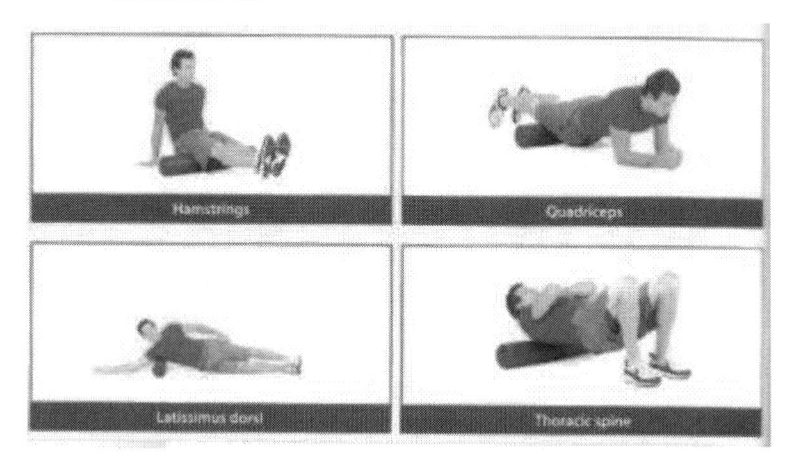

https://victorsrunningblog.wordpress.com/tag/myofascial-release

You may not need to make many changes or a lot of different adjustments since it's just a welcome workout session. Just assess what body parts are tighter than others or which ones have a certain level of discomfort. Just like other exercise assessments, this will also help your client with the stretching and flexors. Keep telling your client to breathe and don't get fixated on the sensation of massaging.

Battle Ropes Assessment

Battling rope training elicits a metabolic response that exceeds the responses known to occur in the game of basketball. So, if the goal is to improve the metabolic conditioning to enhance court fitness, strategically implementing a battling rope regime, similar to the training session, could be advantageous.

1https://creativemarket.com/master1305/2617745 -Woman-with-battle-ropes-exercise-in-the-fitness-gym.

For upper body conditioning, battle ropes are the best tools available. One can do them while maintaining a squat position and making wave patterns in the air. Whip the ropes in a wave-like motion continuously in sets of repetitions. Battle ropes are determining factors of measuring strength as they operate on the criteria of HIIT (High-Intensity Interval Training).

Kettlebell Swing

The next is **the kettlebell swing** test, which is designed to measure the client's performance and technique. Different types of kettlebell tests can be used in your welcome workout assessment. Some of these tests measure your muscular endurance, cardiovascular endurance, mental toughness, efficiency, handling techniques, etc.

Once you are done with the battle ropes and the kettlebell tests, ask your clients again how they feel on a scale of 1 to 10. By this time, I am pretty sure their stamina would have decreased, so they should probably rate themselves somewhere near 5 to 6 or a maximum of 7. However, if they still rate themselves eight and you see their condition not complying with their words, you need to tell them again that this is not a challenge but an assessment. For both, the Battle Rope and Kettlebell swing, you can use the rate of perceived exertion chart to measure:

1.Okay To Go

2. Very, Very Light Intensity

3. Very Light Intensity

4. Light Intensity

5. Moderate Intensity

6. Moderate To Intense

7. Intense

8. Very Intense

9. Very, Very Intense

10. Maximum Intensity

Plank

https://www.popsugar.com/fitness/Best-Plank-Exercise-Flat-Abs-38746525

The next set of exercises is the **plank**, which is very important. The Plank test, also referred to as the Prone Bridge test, is a simple fitness test. It assesses core muscle strength and can also be used as an exercise to improve core strength. However, since we haven't yet moved to the fitness planning step, we will only be using it as a measure to test for core muscle strength. Note that you may add additional weights (not too heavy, around 20 to 40 lbs.) to increase the intensity of the exercise, but that depends on how your client is doing after all these previous exercises.

You wouldn't want to scare them away right after the welcome workout assessment. You want to retain them!

The aim of the Plank test is to hold the plank position for a required period. Its primary purpose is to measure endurance and control of the back stabilizing muscle. However, to execute a plank, you need:

- A stopwatch
- A flat and clean surface
- Pen
- Recording sheets

The test aims to assess for how long your clients can endure maintaining the plank position, or if they can complete the sets of time intervals as decided by you. Start by the upper body being supported off the ground with the help of elbows and forearms. Straighten the legs with the weight taken by the toes. The hip is to be lifted off the ground creating a straight line from head to toe. Start the stopwatch and make sure the head is facing forward and not looking downwards. The plank can be very tough for many people, so you may not want to overburden your clients on the very first day. Go by the intervals of 10 seconds and gradually increase them to 15 and then 20 (with or without additional weights).

Once you are satisfied with the assessment, you may stop the reps and then proceed by taking it to the table (we will discuss this in the later chapters).

Summary

To carry out Welcome Workout Assessment of your client, follow the pattern in the following manner (although adjustable on the circumstances):

SET 1

- 10 Seconds Battle Ropes
- 10 Seconds Kettlebell
- 10 Seconds Plank

After Set 1, ask your client how they feel on a scale of 1 to 10 (10 being the worst), and proceed accordingly.At this point, you need to observe client's expression and judge how far do you need to go.

Set 2

For Set 2, repeat the same process.

Note:

Welcome workout sessions play a significant role in a personal training journey. In simple words, clients' fitness starts with a welcome workout with the trainer. The findings from the session help trainers etch out the most suitable fitness plan for clients by taking into account all the evaluations and determine the best path to meet the clients' goals. Moreover, once assessed, short and long term goals can be discussed.

From here, the client and trainer establish a personal bond **that** builds a platform for planning a suitable workout plan depending on the goals, needs, requirements, and financial feasibility. Together, you'll create a personalized timeline for reaching milestones. As a trainer, you will provide an overview of cardio and weight equipment (if needed) and lead your client through a quick one-on-one workout to get them comfortable with the process.

Chapter 6 Body Composition Test and Body Fat Analyzer

Do you know your current body weight on the scales? I bet most of you reading this would answer in the affirmative. But do you know your actual body composition, your body fat percentage, your water weight, and the composition of lean muscle mass that makes up for the proportions of your body?

Well, most of us don't! As per the prevailing practice, we gauge our health status by either measuring our total body weight on the scale or by calculating our Body Mass Index (BMI: the ratio between your weight and height). This thumb rule is so widely in practice that even in the medical community, practitioners determine your health status as either fat, obese, underweight, or normal, by just looking at the stand-alone integers. However, these numbers are not always right. The readings obtained may determine your overall body measurement of one or two types, but in any case, this does not measure how healthy or unhealthy a body is. Even for three different people with the same height and body weight, there will be three possibilities of varying body compositions. Let's consider Person A, Person B, and Person C. All three of them have different body types, but their heights and body weight are the same – say, 5'8 and 170 lbs., respectively. If these three were to go for a health check-up by using the typical body weight and BMI methods, they all would fall in the same category –underweight, overweight, or healthy. However, without considering such critical information as the body composition and body fat percentage, the health care provider overlooks essential data that can be an indication of probable cardiovascular diseases.

Speaking of that, as per the criteria set by these simple tests (total body weight or BMI), a typical athlete who eats clean and trains every day would fall in the category of being obese or overweight considering their height and body weight. But are they obese?

The answer is NO! Their body composition will be less fat accumulated and more lean muscle, also known as protein mass, which reduces their chances of health risks such as cardiovascular diseases (unless genetic).

So what is the solution? Well, we live in the modern era, and we need not stick to outdated practices. We need to adopt, adapt, and upgrade as per current standards and requirements. One solution to determine your body health status is through understanding your body composition test. What is it? Let's find out.

Body Composition Test

What does the reading on the weighing scale represent? When you step on the scale, the reading does not determine how much fat or muscle composition your body has. All you see is the ‘heaviness’ of your weight.

The body composition test is a non-invasive body analyzer that goes beyond just the weighing scale readings. It provides detailed data of your body weight by breaking it down to significant sub-determinants such as fat, muscle, and water. The results are then obtained on a standardized Result Sheet.

Body composition test can take anywhere from 15 seconds to 120 seconds. The test is very 'client-friendly' as it causes the least discomfort to the customer; its advanced technology requires neither pinching nor dunking, and you can get credible information that can be used to achieve your fitness, health, and body goals with actionable objectives and precision. SHowever, to offer this insight to your clients, you should be able to interpret the body composition result sheet correctly. If used properly, the body composition test result sheet can be one of the most powerful tools at your disposal to train, guide, and care for your clients in newer ways that weren't possible before the crack of this innovation.

To harvest the maximum benefit of this test result, you need to learn how to interpret the data – what does the information that the sheet contains says to you? And more importantly, what can you do with this information?

The Body Composition test result sheet comes with important information related to health and fitness that any fitness/health instructor would consider for the wellness of their clients. You need to learn what the terms on the result sheet mean, their value, and what your next steps should be in the fitness routine as per the obtained results. You use this data to strategically elevate the graph of your clients and your business' wellbeing.

Body Fat Analyzer

We have reached great heights of undiscovered technical milestones, which were seemingly impossible before, and are soon expecting a new wave of technological revolution. However, even with tremendous technological integration, we are unsure about the precision of body fat measurement. With most of the commercially available body fat analyzers, it is difficult to get accurate body fat readings.

For the sake of ease, thankfully, there is not just one way to conduct body fat assessment. There are multiple other options, similar to generating results, available for body analysis.

As there are different types of impedance meters (another name for body fat analyzers) available in the market for the general audience, the results obtained from them also vary. See, it's a matter of how advanced of a technological gadget you are using and also which approach you are taking to conduct the test.

In addition to the technological grading, there are other factors as well that can influence the body fat readings, such as how hydrated you were at the time of recording the measurement.

If your client is particular about their body fat analysis, and they cut no slack over the precision range, then you may refer them to a physician for more accurate measurement techniques. However, since we are looking for workable solutions within a fitness institution, having an approximate evaluation will do just fine for us.

Depending on the circumstances and requirements, other available options may include:

Dual Energy X-Ray Absorptiometry: Unlike regular X-Ray reports, this is a specialized X-ray exam conducted to obtain information about more than just the bones. This method provides detailed information about the ratios between the muscles, fat, and bones in different parts of your body.

Air Displacement Plethysmography: Previously, we introduced the method of containing a body in a pod-like shell. Well, this technique is similar to that. With this approach, your client or the person whom the test is being conducted on is enclosed in an egg-shaped computerized chamber, also known as bod pod. The device then proceeds to take specific measurements of their body density, weight, and volume to perform simple calculations. These evaluations are used to calculate your body fat percentage.

Underwater Weighing: This is an interesting one. Underwater weighing is also known as hydro densitometry, but don't get confused by this complex term. It's a simple method where a person has to sit on a unique chair submerged in water. Their underwater weight and body density is then used to calculate the body fat presence and its total composition in the body.

In addition to these, body fat percentages can also be measured (or estimated) through several other cross-sectional imaging methods such as Computerized Tomography, Nuclear Magnetic Resonance Spectroscopy, and MRI (Magnetic Resonance Imaging). These scans, although challenging to operate at a body fitness center, can provide the most accurate body fat percentages, especially for intra-abdominal fat measurements. These scans are usually expensive and not used for measuring body fat.

A sonogram is another method of calculating body fat in specific body parts. However, as their fitness consultant and trainer, you can always ask your clients to get any of these scans done if you find it very important for the cause of the fitness program.

To obtain data specific to only body composition analysis and body measurements, there are different health promotion centers and coaches specified for the task. These people are not trainers and do not provide any kind of assistance in fitness training. They only conduct health promotion appointments. These appointments perform several tests and obtain information regarding people's weight, height, blood pressure, BMI (Body Mass Index), and Body Fat Percentage. If you do not have the facility of measuring body fat at your fitness center, you can always refer your clients to get their test reports from any of these centers.

Before starting any of my clients' training programs, I invest enough time in understanding them and their bodies completely to help them see how their bodies will respond under different 'pressures.' It's an enriching part of my work to help people understand their health risks and assist them with several ways of reducing such risks.

Many people are interested to know how **BIA (Body Impedance Analysis)** works. Their curiosity is more driven by the will to see if it actually works. It is a handheld device for calculating body fat percentage. And yes, it works!

The device sends a harmless small electrical signal throughout the body. The machine then detects the speed it takes for the message to travel across the different body parts, depending on the amount of fat their body parts contain. The slower the signal, the higher the fat percentage will be. The case is opposite if the signal travels faster, the faster the speed, the lesser the body fat percentage.

When it comes to accuracy, a handheld BIA device has about a ± 3.5-5% margin of error. To obtain the best results for their body fat percentage test, clients must avoid drinking alcohol, showering, exercising, consuming a large meal, drinking a large amount of water, and such body tampering actions before their readings are taken.

Overall, though, the BIA can get a reasonable estimate of an individual's body fat percent while being quick and painless. Part of taking control of your health means getting to know your numbers, including body fat percentage and body mass index!

Reading the Body Composition test

Body Composition Analysis

	Values	Total Body Water	Lean Body Mass	Weight
Intracellular Water (lbs)	70.5	109.6	149.9	163.3
Extracellular Water (lbs)	39.0			
Dry Lean Mass (lbs)	40.3			
Body Fat Mass (lbs)	13.4			

Figure Source: ***https://inbodyusa.com/general/result-sheet-interpretation/***

Starting from above, first, you have the **Intercellular water** and **Extracellular water** readings. Intercellular water, as the term suggests, is the amount of water that your body's cells hold. On the other hand, extracellular water reading is related to the amount of water outside the cells. Summed up, it makes for Total Body Water.

For better insights, both the sections contain useful information about body health status. However, monitoring extracellular water, in particular, has a lot to say about a person's health. For instance, if you notice an increase in extracellular water but not in intercellular water, this could be an indication of swelling or inflammation.

Body Composition Analysis

	Values	Total Body Water	Lean Body Mass	Weight
Intracellular Water (lbs)	70.5	109.6	149.9	163.3
Extracellular Water (lbs)	39.0			
Dry Lean Mass (lbs)	40.3			
Body Fat Mass (lbs)	13.4			

Figure Source: https://inbodyusa.com/general/result-sheet-interpretation/

After the ECW and ICW, there's a section of **DLM (Dry Lean Mass).** This information is related to the weight of mineral content and protein within the body. Although this section is often underused, the data can reveal some interesting facts about your physical health.

Since DLM is not made up of any water and is purely a product of protein, if you notice an increase in DLM value, your client has likely gained muscle.

Body Composition Analysis

	Values	Total Body Water	Lean Body Mass	Weight
Intracellular Water (lbs)	70.5	109.6	149.9	163.3
Extracellular Water (lbs)	39.0			
Dry Lean Mass (lbs)	40.3			
Body Fat Mass (lbs)	13.4			

Below DLM, there's **Body Fat Mass**. It is an essential section as most of the diseases are linked to the findings of this section's results. It reports all of the person's body fat, including both the internal (visceral) level and surface level (subcutaneous).

Figure Source: *https://inbodyusa.com/general/result-sheet-interpretation/*

Once you have obtained all three values, you add the ECW, ICW, and DLM together, and you will get the total **Lean Body Mass (LBM),** shown in the column second to full-body water. LBM is the weight of everything that is in the body, except for the fat. It includes water, muscles, organs, bones, and everything that is not fat.

Body Composition Analysis

	Values	Total Body Water	Lean Body Mass	Weight
Intracellular Water (lbs)	70.5	109.6	149.9	163.3
Extracellular Water (lbs)	39.0			
Dry Lean Mass (lbs)	40.3			
Body Fat Mass (lbs)	13.4			

Figure Source: https://inbodyusa.com/general/result-sheet-interpretation/

Most often, the increase in **LBM** refers to an increase in muscle, which is an improvement in the body. However, people who do not maintain standard body water ratios may have increased LBM due to inflammation or swelling caused by certain health conditions.

The Importance of the Body Composition test – Reasons Why You Need It!

Understand Your Weight

Don't just measure your weight, *read* it. Read what it says and then do the necessary. Weight alone is a poor health indicator as it cannot distinguish fat from muscle. Through the Body Composition test, you get the breakdown analysis of your body composition, which helps determine body health issues, if any.

Set Your Goals

Through the Body Composition test results, you can measure your body fat ratios, which will give a more appropriate measure of how healthy you are than BMI. Knowing your exact body composition helps you set clear goals, telling you whether you need to cut down bodyweight or just lose the fat.

Measure Your Strength

See which exercises bring out the best results in you. It can be done before and after test comparison or just casually to know how much muscle development has taken place in your arms, legs, etc.

Track Your Progress

It's not just about knowing body composition. Body Composition test allows you to monitor and track changes in your body, once your baseline is set.

By using body composition values such as fat percentages and muscle mass percentages as a measure of progress, you can keep track of how well your clients are doing. Also, if you see no change in their 'weight,' you can show them the loss in body fat and gain in muscle mass, which is an excellent situation.

Often when people work out, their muscle mass rises, and body fat drops. This cancels out the reading impact on overall body weight. It means, although the internal work is good, you might not be able to see the change unless you perform a Body Composition test. For some people, continuous feedback is essential as it serves as motivation. It keeps people driven to continue on their path toward a healthier lifestyle while achieving positive body goals.

Have More Targeted Workout Sessions

When you know your body composition, you know what to work for and what to work against – for instance, muscle and fat composition. It helps you choose a suitable workout program for your client, which is not just useful on the outside but also on the inside.

This Body Composition test is a fantastic testing tool to assess your health. Determining health composition will not only help you reduce any possible risks of diseases but will also allow you to understand your body in depth. You will learn to read your body beyond what just the reading on the scale says.

If you want to live a healthy lifestyle, try your best to eat a healthy diet. Whether you work out to keep your body weight under control, are an athlete trying to optimize your health, or you just want to understand your body and your potential risk for disease, the Body Composition testing might be right for you.

I believe in taking precautions and preventing problems before they even occur; remember, prevention is always better than cure. A Body Composition test is a vital tool for your clients, which will help you understand the current situation of their bodies. What kind of help do they need, and what is most suitable for them?

Using the Body Composition test will help you notice the changes occurring inside your body throughout the whole process. It will help you keep track of your overall health and what you can do to take it to the next level. It will help you select the most suitable plan for your client, and will also help in mitigating the risk of any possible workout consequences.

So stop worrying about the numbers on the weighing scale, and start looking at the bigger picture. Take a test, analyze the results, and then proceed accordingly in the direction you think is the best for your clients!

Chapter 7
Back to the Table

Continuing with the discussion, performing initial assessments (through a welcome workout) is a great way to lay the foundation for lasting relationships with your potential clients. Assessments play an integral role in the process of closing any fitness deal. These assessments are an embodiment of professionalism that showcase the trainer's knowledge and develop clients' confidence in the trainer's ability and skills.

Fitness trainers focus clients' attention on genuine investment in determining their specific goals and designing the most suitable customized health programs based on drawn results. These results are either observed, asked, or verbally communicated through a session of meet and greet (as discussed in chapter 2). When you invest in your clients, it is much likely they will invest in you and the services you are to offer them. Once the assessment session is over, it's time to take things to the next level – time for some table talk! Explaining the results to clients is a crucial element and a pivotal card in closing any fitness deal. It is one of the most prominent qualities of a competent trainer to ***Dictate Features as Potential Benefits*** to the client. You wouldn't want to mess this up!

From the Floor to the Table

Let's take it down from the floor to the table and take a look at the things you need to discuss during a one-on-one session. Table talks are really a fun part as you get to show your clients your smarter, wittier, skilled, and qualified side. Although before you begin, be aware that you are dealing with a client. Whether you are signing them, assessing them through a pre-workout session, or inquiring about their fitness goals, remember they are observing you too. The assessment is always a two-way road, so you want to be careful of what you convey of yourself.

You can start your conversation with something like: *"Mike, it was a good session we had there on the floor. Thank you for letting me analyze your physical body structure. Now let's get to the details and look at some results. I am sure you are as excited to get to know your performance as I am. Here are some of my observations."*

"First, I noticed while you were standing, your shoulders fell a little forward from where they really should be. Also, they were slightly internally rotated. This indicates that you have some weakness in your lower/mid-back muscles and some tightness in muscles where it supposedly shouldn't be. It is understandable from the routine you have... "

And the conversation goes forth from there. What is worth noticing here is the tone and the use of words. You don't have to come off as harsh to your clients as some times many people are body dysmorphic. Someone telling them about the anomaly hurts their confidence and pushes them back into their insecurities – you don't want that. You want to retain a client. So, your tone should be more empathetic and understanding.

Then, you can continue with: *"Also Mike, I noticed while you were planking, your back curve wasn't aligned the way it should have been. This indicates weakness in your core muscles and tightness in your hip flexors. It is understandable that since you have never had any prior experience of fitness training, this must be a lot for you right now. But don't worry. This is what I am here for. We will make this happen together."*

"So I have decided that while designing your program, I will center my focus on strengthening your back muscles and stretching your internal shoulder rotators. The program I will design for you will emphasize strengthening your core muscles, which includes your hip and back muscles, your abdominal muscles, and your hip flexors".

"One more thing I observed is that you were a little tighter on the left side of your body than the right side. And no, I am not speaking of balancing, but generally, you were having difficulty while performing certain exercises. This happens when a body is out of alignment or if the body structure is disoriented due to sitting in the same position for long hours."

"I'm sure you would want your body alignment to get back to its orientation to save you from any further wear and tear injury. Due to this specific muscle, the surrounding muscles are also getting affected. That's hindering your free body movement. So it seems like you will need more than just physical training. We are not going to make any rigid movements but will allow the body to adapt to new changes and then make further serious changes as we progress one milestone to the next."

"During our session, when you stretch, I will spend a little while focusing on the left side, particularly to check if that helps develop better symmetry. Once we get there, we will see how your body feels towards that. Sounds good?"

By this point, the client will typically be impressed by your observations. They will see that you pay attention to the details. Clients are attracted and feel more familiar with the surroundings once they begin to feel considered, recognized, and counted. Most trainers end up losing their client deals in the last stages due to wrong assumptions made in the name of observations just to bag the deal. No, you don't want to be unfair! You need to be very careful. Being a fitness trainer is more than just a job; it's a responsibility and a commitment.

You don't need to bombard your client with a difficult-to-understand jargon. Take a more scientific approach to the training program. Dictate your ability to customize the program according to their specific body type.

Once you get to this point, the further 'sales' conversation will be easy and smooth for you. From here on, your next opening statement can be: *"Excellent, Mike. Now all that is left to do is decide how you and I are going to work together toward achieving your desired fitness goals, as well as reaching a much better level of health status from what you are at right now."*

Listen Carefully and Know the 'Why'

As an effective trainer, one of the most important lessons here is to be an effective listener. You need to be efficient in communication, and that includes both speaking and listening. Effective communication comprises of both the elements of two way conversation feedback. You really need to listen to what the client has to say and get to know the "WHY" behind their motive to join a fitness program. We will get to this part later in this chapter. For now, let's focus on what you are going to talk about 'on the table.'

Since you are dealing with live clientele in real-time, there are no scripts or rebuttals. You need to prepare yourself for every type of client that walks in through that door and learn the art to make them stay – you need to be able to retain a potential client.

Since most of our clients are going to come to you for either losing or managing their weight, it is critical for your understanding and workout process to record their baseline measurements. This will help trainers to monitor their clients' progress and also ensure clients' satisfaction that you are leading them in the right direction i.e. towards achieving body-positive goals.

By this time, you must have already taken the skinfold measurements, girth measurements, body weight, and overall body composition. Keep that data saved in the clients' files from the beginning of the programs. Take a photo if required to provide an objective assessment of program results as well as the progress made.

You might be wondering why there is so much emphasis on pre-assessments and performance analysis. Well, these observations and numbers don't just help trainers understand their clients better, but they also give them the advantage to show their concern regarding their clients' health and goals. It serves as an objective tool to demonstrate strengths, weaknesses, and to monitor progress.

Pre-assessments direct customized fitness program design. My studio's performance assessment consists of different sets of exercises, and I believe yours must have some other, or maybe the same. But the point is to assess clients before signing them. There is a set of particular exercises that you must include in your criteria of assessment. I have provided that criteria in chapter 5, known as the Welcome Workout Assessment.

The next step of the conversation is listening. Before we move ahead toward structuring and planning a workout, we need to ask the clients about their goals. That's because, without a goal, an exercise would be just a walk in the park. To achieve the maximum result of the effort made, one needs to have sentiments involved. That's how you bring out the best in your clients.

As a part of baseline assessments, a trainer should first ask the client what the biggest obstacles according to them are. Trainers need to find out what made their clients fall previously. Also, this will be a great time to clear any misinformation that the client might have in their head about myths associated with the program.

Ask if the client were close and if they failed; also, determine the reasons. It may be that they couldn’t control their diet due to which, even after training for months, they were standing from where they started – no progress. A trainer could use this opportunity to introduce them to healthy eating and nutrition plans while also briefing them about cardiovascular training and resistance training to boost their body mechanism.

Be a Coach, Not Just a Trainer

The next thing that trainers need to ask their clients about is their most pressing goals – linked with their SEEs (Significant Emotional Experiences) most of the time.

Most times, clients' goals are derived from their significant emotional experience, and trainers should learn the "WHY" behind it. You must discover the real motive behind the client's decision to opt for the program.

Knowing the WHY is crucial in fitness training for multiple reasons, the biggest of which is optimum results. When the emotional element is in sync with physical effort, the results achieved bring inner peace, joy, and satisfaction as the client progresses towards achieving their goals.

So, to keep your clients' attention and interest intact, the trainer should ask clients their most important goals – both short-term and long-term. This will help the client as well as the trainer to get on the same page. As a trainer, you wouldn't want to get stuck in a position where what the client is looking for is a weight loss program, and you keep boring them by talking about the liberating feeling of a workout. You need to press the right buttons to get the clients motivated.

For instance, if a female client is seeking to reduce her lower body weight and get toned, and all you keep telling her is about gaining mass, you might push her away. To provide the right motivation and the most suitable plan according to her needs and goals, you need to give her the space to speak about her goals.

This helps the trainer to figure out each client's motivational trigger and put them to correct use.

The other factors that you need to discuss and evaluate before presenting the client with the four fundamentals of the training program are the health factor. You need to account for the medical details to avoid any future mishaps.

Exercise, especially exercise done in a fitness studio, involves bearing some stress levels. This stress may cause a change in internal body systems, which might bring up any underlying health issues, for instance, dehydration, illness, fatigue, etc. Or it could be just the intensity of the program that is going 'too hard' for a client's current health status. You wouldn't want a client throwing up all over the floor; this can be problematic for you both.

For this reason, a fitness trainer must collect enough information regarding the health of the client during the consultation and observe any type of extreme responses that occur in clients after the exercise. This is one of the reasons I reinforce a welcome workout assessment.

However, there are two types of factors that are important while concluding a client's file and offering them the kind of plan to follow:

- Modifiable factors. These are factors that can be worked upon to improve or change—for example, lifestyle, smoking habits, cholesterol levels, etc.
- Non-modifiable factors. These are things you can't change but adapt to accordingly—for example, age, genetic disorders, family medical history.

Measurable risk factors such as blood pressure, cholesterol, and body fat percentage and blood glucose levels are recorded more often as we get older. This is due to a general fact that as we age, our risk factor increases.

Risk factors are recorded to assess any harm that may be caused to the client's body due to the change in lifestyle, workout, and eating and sleeping routine. This type of change is for good, but not in every single case. So, it is always advisable to ask your clients for any medical specifications beforehand. This may also include asking them about any allergies because you will also design their nutrition chart if you want to put them on track of achieving specific goals, i.e., muscle gain or weight loss.

One outstanding quality of exceptional trainers is that they realize that helping clients achieve their fitness goals is not just about the exercise regime and nutrition advice. There's a mindset element to the journey that is as important as any physical variable. Significant emotional experience plays a vital role in shaping clients' performance and the results of their workout. This mindset element is essential to ensure that clients make the most out of their program.

To help you understand the emotional link, you need to walk the extra mile with your client and understand them as a coach. Being a great coach plays a big part in becoming a successful personal trainer.

Good coaching helps trainers in keeping their clients motivated and retained for a longer period. It develops a mutual bond of trust between the trainer and the client. This mutually shared and understood element gives you a clear direction on how to design a unique training program for each client to help them achieve optimum health.

Chapter 8
The Four Foundations

Let’s delve into the second section of the table talk. There is more about personal fitness consultancy than just compiling a list of exercises for the clients to perform. You want to make sure that as a personal trainer, you get your clients the maximum out of the plan they choose. Following the welcome workout assessment and the table talk, explaining the four fundamentals of training programs plays an essential role in shaping clients' minds.

All of the factors, including the clients’ health objectives, current health and fitness status, diseases, lifestyle and goals, influence the nature of the training program. Each human body varies from the other, and so, it cannot be treated the same way. As discussed previously, two people with the same height and same weight will be differently treated depending on their body composition.

The influence of the factors above covers all physical and technical demands, exercise movements, workout hours, the choice of activities, and the environment as well. Keeping in account all the previously obtained information, the program must be tailored to the clients' essentials (what their body demands and requires), while also covering main physical development areas such as:

- Overall physique
- Healthy gains
- Reduced fat levels
- Muscular fitness
- Cardiovascular fitness
- Flexibility
- Core stability

By this time, the trainer would already know their clients' goals and what they have in mind. However, sometimes many clients walk in to the trainers with unrealistic expectations and goals. As an effective trainer, you need to evaluate first what their body **needs** while also keeping in mind what the client **demands**.

The key to successful client consultation is to work for the body requirements while still reflecting on the agreed goals between the client and the trainer. You can do that by allocating appropriate frequency, volume, intensity, and time to each activity. The exercise choice should also be made according to what is most suitable for the clients' objectives and capabilities.

The equipment, resources, and the exercise environment available to the trainer also determine the potential scope of training and its progress. A skilled professional trainer can improvise without compromising on safety. They sketch out the most suitable plan with the most effective exercises within the available resources and affordability of the client.

One can opt for different ways when entering a fitness institute. Well, you see fitness is not just about muscle building – sometimes people just want to do cardio or aerobics to lose fat by burning calories. For a person seeking to lose fat by burning calories, you would not suggest a strength training program. Instead, you will put them on HIIT training, as that is the most effective way for them to lose weight, along with dietary and nutrition supplementation. Similar is the case with varying goals and different body types, as well as current health status evaluation.

An exercise program doesn't need to be unnecessarily complicated to be effective. We need to be mindful that any type of exercise lays physical stress on the human body, and can change internal body regulation. So, keeping the endurance and stress endurance ability in mind, trainers should manipulate or tweak a few variables such as repetitions, intensity, or rest cycle. This way, they can vary the outcomes of the program for each individual.

The Four Foundations of a fitness program talks about reviewing the principles and variables of program design. It discusses how these foundations can be applied to create results for each client based on distinctive conditions.

This chapter discusses the fundamental principles of designed program variables and how the client can adapt these.

Research can provide some insight into how the human body may adapt to an exercise stimulus, but factors responsible for each individual's specific training outcome include:

- Current health status
- Previous training experience
- Hydration
- Body composition

- Any injuries
- Age
- Gender
- Genetic profile
- Goals
- Diseases
- Nutritional intake
- Lifestyle

I have carefully evaluated all the influential factors and have landed on the four fundamentals of a well-planned maximum health achieving plan which are:

- Progressive Fitness Targets and Professional Fitness Assistance
- Progressive Nutrition Program
- Progressive Cardiovascular Training Program
- Progressive Strength Training Program

Progressive Fitness Targets and Professional Fitness Assistance

Working out can be intimidating, especially if you have no prior experience. It is normal to have goals and be unsure about how to achieve them – this is what mentors, guides, teachers, and trainers are for. A personal trainer can help you overcome any such problems, including the lack of motivation as they know the core reasons behind any motive.

For instance, clients who work out on their own may end up losing motivation when they don't see their bodies achieving their desired goals. It is either due to the unrealistic expectations that the client has set or the lack of education – knowledge about what their body wants. They keep on doing the hard work, but they don't reach anywhere – why? It is because of not knowing where to apply their energy.

Professional trainers, through their knowledge and skills, help clients channel their efforts in the right direction to obtain the maximum effect, restoring client satisfaction and motivation. In maximizing the effectiveness of exercise and reducing the risk of injury, personal trainers put together a perfect routine to fix the clients' movements and postures to help them achieve their goals.

Also, working with a trainer helps you progress more in shorter periods, overcoming one of the biggest hurdles of time. For instance, let's say, if a client wants to work with me as their personal trainer, I will decide with them the number of sessions they are okay to take according to their routine.

Let's say they have to come to the gym four days a week; they can allocate two days to work out with me and the remaining two to work on strength, cardiovascular or resistance training. They can even take one session of two hours per week and then adjust the remaining workout doing exercises as guided by me on the other days. A detailed live discussion of this foundation will also help clients overcome any money objection.

Progressive Nutrition Program

Nutrition is one of the essential pillars of a healthy lifestyle. About 70% of your fitness training results are dependent on what you eat when you eat and how much you eat it. One of the keys to a healthy, sustainable lifestyle is proper nutrition. Your health can be improved by keeping a delicate balance between your activities, the food you consume, and supplementation. However, with the availability of millions of options, advice, opinions, and possibilities, it is very easy to become confused when it comes to health and nutrition. People are misguided in the name of achieving unrealistic goals by following the path that is leading their health to decline further. However, I have combined a series of healthy tips in a sequence that will aid my reader to achieve their body goals by staying on the right track.

My focus is not on providing my clients with a "DIET" but a "LIFESTYLE." I do that because diets are temporary and can be easily cheated on, whereas lifestyle is usually lasting. Once adopted, it can lead to long-term beneficial effects on one's health. The key here to remember is that there are no short cuts if you are looking for permanent solutions.

Stabilizing health takes time. All you need to do is be determined and follow your diet routine as guided by your health instructor. This will help you achieve better results in the desired time.

Being healthy is not about staying unrealistically thin, putting strict restrictions by fasting all the time, or even depriving yourself of your favorite food. Instead, it is about improving health, feeling great, boosting your mood, and having more energy to perform tasks.

As a trainer, define a suitable healthy eating plan together with your client, considering their goals. For instance, if the client's goal is to lose weight, you will start by asking them to restrict their calories to 2000 max a day. Not just that, along with the food consumption, you may have to put them on High-Intensity Interval Training or thermodynamics trick to burn more calories than they consume.

Let's say, if your client is consuming 1500 calories a day and burning 2000 every day, they are collectively losing 3500 calories per week. This way they will lose 1 pound of weight per week.

Of course, as important a diet is, there are supplements and diet specifications also. You need to amend dietary patterns and nutritional intake accordingly for your clients, depending on their medical health conditions as well.

Eating healthy does not have to be unnecessarily complicated. If you are overwhelmed by all the conflicting diet advice and nutrition guides out there, then you are not alone. It seems for every expert advice you get about how a particular food is very good for your health, you will find another piece of advice contradicting the previous one.

Progressive Cardiovascular Training Program

Cardiovascular training is an important component of any fitness program. While the rest of the exercises focus on transforming your physical body shape, cardiovascular training helps regulate smooth internal bodily systems. In addition to any other muscle group that you use, when you do cardio, you provide your heart, lungs, and blood vessels a good workout – internal conditioning.

Cardiovascular exercises are extremely important as they help run your body's engine smoothly. And without a strong engine, a body can go nowhere.

A cardiovascular training program can be opted for separately or incorporated along with the other type of training program, depending on the need and clients' prospectus. However, whether the goal is to lose weight, increase endurance, or build muscle, cardiovascular exercise is effective and efficient.

No two people have the same fitness goals, which is why it is vital to have a variety of tools in your arsenal to help clients increase their cardiovascular endurance and improve overall health. Different types of cardiovascular training are:

- HIIT Cardio
- Long Slow Distance Cardio
- Anaerobic Interval Training
- Cross-Training
- Circuit Training
- Fartlek Training

In addition to heart and lungs conditioning, cardiovascular exercise serves as a primary tool for weight management as it helps burn calories.

For example, walking, jogging, and running burn approximately 100 calories per mile covered. So, walking two miles each way to and from work will burn off the equivalent of a pound of body fat in a fortnight! Also, you will tone up the muscles employed, usually the legs, and release endorphins during exercise. Endorphins are the 'feel-good' hormones that give you that buzz after a workout.

Progressive Strength Training Program

Last but not least, another fundamental component of a well-equipped fitness program is the progressive strength training program. Progressive resistance or progressive strength is a training method in which overload is substantially increased to facilitate adaptation. This foundation is fundamental for weight loss, muscle building, and gaining stamina.

Your body adapts to changes constantly pressured through fitness training, which is very important. In order to observe muscle growth and improved fitness levels, you need to keep challenging your body with new difficulties and changed patterns after every interval, as the same routine may stall your progress. If your goal is to lose weight, it puts you at risk for a weight loss plateau, that frustrating time when your weight loss starts to stall.

Strength or resistance training challenges your muscle endurance and helps you build stronger than usual counterforce. Muscles become stronger by progressively using heavier weights or by increasing resistance. This type of exercise is essential to increase muscle mass, strengthen bones, or tone muscles.

Chapter 9
Closing

It all boils down to closing. As a personal trainer, there’s no step more important than closing the deal or sale.

Most of the fitness trainers feel nervous as they reach this step because of the sensitivity – this is a make or break situation. All the rapport built with the prospective client leads to this step. So it is understandable to be a little nervous, but don't lose your chill!

Just as with any goal worth striving for. What makes the success of a sale so rewarding is the amount of detail that goes into it. And also, it is always nice to get paid for your quality service!

It's all about the client. Most of the personal trainers capable of closing the client's consultancy, be it online or personal, know that the mantra is fixing the prospective client's problem. These successful trainers know or have learned the psychological art of helping potential clients' queries by providing them with a nudge or a cue, which triggers their brain to decide to move ahead and finally close the deal with you – the trainer. All that you need to do is be strategic, client-centric, and goal-oriented.

No matter what type of product it is, potential customers always tend to raise objections for all kinds of sales pitches. However, when it comes to selling personal fitness/personal training, the consultant has to be prepared for more strident objection.

Some people are immune to their normal lifestyle, so much so that any type of change in their routine becomes a hurdle for them. Most of the time, this is due to a lack of motivation or an unclear perspective of how things go at a fitness institute.

Persuading people to change their lifestyle and adopt healthy habits to shift their sleeping, eating, and exercising patterns can be notoriously tricky. It's also tough to fight the perception that hiring a personal trainer is an unnecessary indulgence.

Learning to overcome those objections means the difference between a successful personal training practice and one that struggles under the weight of constant rejection. Below are some of the objections that a prospective client may raise. As an effective fitness trainer, you should know how to confront their queries and finally close the deal.

Money Objection

One of the biggest hurdles between table talk and deal signing is money objection. Even the most interested client may object to the price, but you don't need to wait for that moment to prepare yourself.

Prepare in advance and think about positive responses to such objections. For instance, if such a situation arises, you need to solve their confusion and recall in comparison to how cost-effective the program is. They might spend more on a night out than they would on a training session. This is an investment opportunity for them – an investment that would help them positive results for their health and body.

What most of the clients really mean when they raise money concern is that they don't see the value in the service. Some of them think they are good with only a gym membership without investing in themselves by hiring personal fitness.

In any sales pitch, when countering money objection, be specific about both what you are offering and what it will cost. Be prepared with flexible and dynamic packages with specific prices for your sessions, as well as with different levels of training experiences with one or two lower-cost options.

Dictate the Features as Potential Benefits

Prepare to outline your value and tell potential clients why you are worth the price – even brag a little where required. Outline what working with a trainer can provide over merely working out at the gym. Include benefits like accountability, motivation, progress monitoring, and a better chance of hitting goals more quickly. Here's a quick pattern to go through while answering money matters:

- Hear it out
- Feed the objection back
- Question it
- Isolate
- Answer
- Confirm

Needing the Permission Objection

Most people have second thoughts before buying a personal training program. They tend to think they need permission to focus on self-improvement, claiming they want to talk to their mates about paying for personal training before making any decisions.

You need to remind such clients that personal health is a legitimate expense, just like every other essential such as clothing, shelter, and food. If the objection still stands strong, you can respect the client's concern and their need to consult about finances.

Time Objection

This is probably another most frequently raised issue by the prospective client. Prepare yourself to hear it very often once you start closing the training sessions. Time's precious, and for some, very precious. Many people can have problems managing time, and this is why you need to find a way around it.

To solve this objection, you may need to ask several questions. This will help you sort out a potential client's schedule by managing the time and number of sessions.

Sit down together and work out a plan that suits the client's schedule but also does not affect your previous client's sessions. Or you can always find a group of people that are willing to work out together, given the specific times.

Ask your prospective client how much time they think they can commit to the training of any kind per week. Just focus on the practicalities here and don't push your services. Once you've determined the time they have, show them what you can offer. Outline the specifics of what you can do together with that time in terms of working out and hitting their goals, even if it's only one hour per week.

To back up your claims, you may also want to offer a guarantee here. A person will be more intrigued and feel encouraged to make time commitment if they know they can look forward to solid, guaranteed results. No, you don't have to make any unrealistic promises. Just make sure the guarantee made is reasonable and time-based.

Also, there are some emotional reasons, in addition to logical ones, that play an important part in closing a fitness consultation. For instance, you might need to deal with some clients in a way that you ask them or challenge them about whether or not they have the discipline and motivation to get in shape. The desire to be better and to improve oneself can serve as a strong emotional trigger to sign the deal.

The drive to improve can be a strong emotion. Prospects who really want to train can overcome their own objections if they feel strongly enough about training themselves into vital, attractive, and healthy people.

Through this book, I have tried to compile key highlights of how to lead in a fitness field. My writings are the dictation of experience I have acquired over the past several years, working as both a trainee and a trainer in the field of health and fitness. I have provided you (the readers) with the tools that you can use to amend fitness consultations. Be it any type of objection while closing a deal, or any hurdle from initial meet and greet to signing the client for the fitness program, this book will serve you as a guide to save your fitness consultations.

In addition to that, the fitness prescription (provided in the early chapters) has been designed carefully, keeping in mind all the accounting notions that go behind signing a prospect client. I want my readers and fellow fitness trainers to use these tools and implement them in their practical professional life processes to yield optimum benefits.

Too many fitness trainers think that their jobs are only limited to planning training programs and completing fitness sessions with clients. However, that is not the complete truth. Knowing how to sell or close a deal is what lies at the core of any successful running fitness business.

So, as a trainer, you are also a business owner. Start embracing the idea that you are also a business professional. This will help you become a better trainer as well as help you make your clients hit their goals.

Start identifying the objections you hear most often and use these tips to plan your own strategies for breaking through them. Don't be afraid to be a salesperson. It's part of who you are now, and that means you can't be afraid to be pushy. Yes, you may put a few people off, but overall you will win more than you will lose.

Chapter 10
A Message to the Readers

As we near the end, I want to tell you that I have put a huge chunk of myself in this book. I hope that it will reflect on all of you as you learn and implement my teachings in your practices.

I believe it is vital for the readers to understand that it is not just the education and skills that make an exceptional personal trainer. Instead, it's a mixed palette of empathy, courage, motivation, understanding, strength, and the drive to improve.

With new fitness institutes opening every week in every other block, you need to stand out among the crowd to make your business strive. To demonstrate outstanding skills and personal trainer qualities, you must really get to know your client. You do not have to be invasive about their personal life and matters they are not comfortable sharing, but learn everything that you think may affect their progress and results. In doing so, the concept of SEE (Significant Emotional Experience) plays a vital role. We have discussed this factor previously in detail (in chapter 3), but it is important to re-emphasize it because of its tremendous value.

Know the 'why' behind a client's decision to join the gym. What are the common reasons for which people around the world join gyms? This part is not only crucial for trainers but also for people who are looking for reasons to step outside their sedentary lifestyle and walk the extra mile, literally. Below are some of the 'prime movers' or prime factors that make clients walk through your doors consistently:

Improved Health: it is no surprise that improved health is a top priority for every individual. This is why it tops the list of prime factors to get the client running.

Weight loss: Weight gain or obesity has been linked to several deadly diseases that not just put people on a fast track to death but also slow down their everyday life.

Looks: Looking better is on everyone's list. By looking better, we do not mean to glamorize a particular body size. Looking better is to be confident in your own body. A healthy workout routine keeps you in shape, spotlighting your best features.

Feel better / Gratification / Boost Self-Esteem: The adage goes, 'Look better to feel better.' People feel better when their health improves. When they are healthy and confident, their inner satisfaction reflects in their physical and mental health.

Seeing positive results, clients feel instant gratification, a sudden boost of self-esteem, which helps them perform better at other life tasks as well.

To stay in shape: A friend who's never been to the gym once said, "Round is a shape." To be fair, he was quite happy with it. However, this approach can be a little confusing. By getting in shape, we mean to promote a healthy body structure.

Tone up: Once you get serious about your health, you look for the possibilities to keep getting better and better each day. For instance, if you have already lost weight, you then seek to work on some muscle or build core strength. Little by little, you climb the stairs of a healthy life by toning up your body. Your goal is to get stronger, build muscle, and chisel away some of the extra fat.

Walking an Extra Mile – Literally!

All of the factors mentioned above sit at the core of any fitness routine – a healthier mind and body. You not only have to tell your client how to achieve better health but guide and direct them to achieve their body goals. You need to tell them that having a healthier physical outlook can help them achieve mental stability and peace.

Many times you might have seen a prominent distinction made between 'body' and 'mind.' However, when considering physical and mental health, these two are interdependent and shouldn't be perceived as separate.

A big part of personal fitness training is to keep your clients motivated and hooked to the defined program. Sometimes they get overwhelmed by the change in lifestyle or the other times they just happen to lose interest. You need to be prepared to deal with both and other similar situations and keep your clients right on track. Teach your client how poor physical health can put their mental health at risk, leading to chances of developing stress and anxiety. It is your primary duty to explain to your clients the importance of health (both physical and mental). These health benefits can be attained once they begin to bring a change in their regular work routine and typical life pattern. Due to modern advances in technology, we have become immune to dependency. We rely on electronic gadgets to get our daily tasks done – something as small as turning on the lights can now be done via a smartphone!

Where technology has a plethora of benefits, at the same time it has normalized a sedentary lifestyle, making people lazier day by day. This regular pattern of life is exposing us to several health risks linked to deadly diseases such as obesity and cardiovascular problems.

As a fitness trainer, it is your job to make sure your client attains good health and consumes a well-balanced diet. Physical fitness not only gets your body in good shape or helps you build muscles, but also promotes longevity and saves you from other health issues. According to studies, physical fitness is as effective as antidepressants for mental health. It has no side effects either! However, there is no 'magic' amount of exercising will it take to get you there; the key is to keep hustling.

The other aspect of keeping your clients in good shape is diet – exercise and nutrition go hand in hand whenever it comes to making the most progress according to the work plan. Diet affects physical health, which can undermine mental health as well. When it comes to advising clients about nutrition, you don't just have to stop them from consuming soda, alcohol, or processed food. But you need to cater to each client's individualities and help them accordingly to eat healthier.

Proper nutrition is a crucial factor that influences the way we feel. While keeping in account different allergies or body reactions, fitness trainers need to come up with a complete plan that does not compromise on an adequate amount of proteins, carbs, vitamins, water, and minerals. Why? Because let me remind you once again, we are establishing a new lifestyle, not just putting our clients on a diet!

Also, many clients might expect you to be knowledgeable. You should know the answers to many nutrition-related queries or eating plans etc. For this reason, you need to prepare in advance and have enough on your hand to satisfy clients' questions. Obviously, no one can ever know everything, but keep yourselves up to date and educated on important and general matters. By the time you grow in this industry, you will become good at handling such situations.

In addition to explaining to your clients the potential benefits of improved health, remind them of the recent pandemic that the world is facing. Covid-19 has taken over the world by the storm, and the numbers are still rising. However, the other side of the story also tells us about focusing on improving health to be able to fight diseases such as Covid-19. And not just that, in fact, when you are healthy, your immunity system boosts up, which makes you strong from the inside – not instantly in the form of muscles. Being healthy from the inside is equally important as being fit from the outside.

Moreover, you want your clients to get the best possible outcomes out of your plan while working with you. This means the effort that needs to be put in is more than just 2 to 4 hours per week that they will be spending with you. They need to eat the right amount of food that supports their fitness goals and the workout routine as you prescribe them.

The Clients and You!

Personal training is a career choice that you may have made as a hobby, or passion, or even a goal. However, once you get into this industry, it's time for you to realize the importance of a fitness trainer in the life of their clients. You do not just have a job, but a responsibility – the responsibility to choose for your clients what's best for them and their health, to change their lifestyle for the better, to help them get on the right track of health and fitness, and to promote longevity and positive body image.

This is why your conduct plays a significant role in shaping the success and durability of your business. Every client is different with their unique set of goals, requirements, and certain restrictions. You need to see clients for not their worth, but how you can help them. Good training is not what is accredited to a 'good client,' but to a 'good trainer'!

This book will help you navigate through fitness loopholes and pitfalls that people run into, even though they try to stay healthy. Health and fitness have become a prominent concern in America because of the rising obesity rate and a reported increase in chronic diseases such as high blood pressures, high cholesterol levels, and diabetes. All these diseases, if not remedied, can lead to a slow death. This book discusses the improvements you can make to your everyday routine for better mental and physical health. It also provides fitness professionals with essential lessons on how to handle a fitness business and run a proper setup. It is divided into three different sections – from when the clients walk through the door to assessing the client and then taking it to the table talk.

The book emphasizes how to become an outstanding fitness trainer and how to lead your clients to follow your guided path. Knowing how to coach your clients to follow the directed workout plan and nutritional habit is essential, regardless of the goal they are trying to achieve. Whether they are on a weight loss or a bodybuilding journey, what goes into their body and its results will determine your success as a personal trainer.

Now, it is up to you to help them understand this and change their lifestyles.

Chapter 11
Conclusion

The clock is ticking. Are you becoming the type of person that you wanted to be?

As we conclude this first book of a series, I believe you have gotten to know me – Tony Deoleo. Who is he to you? What does he do? How is he as a trainer? What does he preach? What is his professional career history?

I have conveyed not just about myself, but a lot about my professional life through this book. I have delivered the keys to unlock doors of achievement in the field of fitness training for both professionals and beginners.

As a personal trainer, as I already said before, you not only need to have education and skills to make people exercise but something else that goes beyond it. I have always treated my clients as projects rather than just 'clients' to whom I owe some hours of service in return for the fee they pay me. Why? Because personal training is much more than that! Personal fitness operates on the delicate horizon of learning humans. The better you are at understanding people, the better you are in the field.

To my fellow fitness readers, always remember, whether you are just stepping into the field of fitness and health wellbeing, or you have already established yourself and worked for a while now, your job is not only a service. It is a responsibility. This is what I practice, and this is what I preach.

Your job is not just to help people lose weight. Your responsibility is to make them feel satisfied from the inside. Make them feel happy once again about their body. You must make people fall in love with themselves again. People often stop caring about themselves as they age, which leads to further destruction of their bodies. You need to restore their faith that they deserve a healthy lifestyle, and so do their bodies.

Sometimes we don’t give it enough thought, but personal trainers don’t just help people drop some pounds. We actually help people buy more laps on the life track. We don’t just help people build core strength, but evoke a sense of satisfaction and self-confidence that helps them in their personal endeavors. Sometimes, we don't just work for wellbeing, but also save people from several other chronic illnesses, which, if they do not care for, would consume them sooner rather than later. As a personal trainer, you always want to keep yourself ahead of others, right? Well, to do so, you need to be at the forefront of the latest information in the fitness world, particularly from a personal training point of view.

Keeping yourself educated will not only help you attain current knowledge about the field dynamics and demographics, but it will also filter down many techniques and ways for you, including the way you deal with clients and business growth. Expanding your overall knowledge is in your total control.

Things can be pretty daunting for you in the field when starting as a personal trainer. Not only are you a little wet behind the ears, but the challenge and risk-taking to emerge in the new game and build a prospective future base is a lot to take. However, things can go pretty smoothly if you break them down and approach strategically.

However, don't worry about what is to come, just be prepared. Make sure you are well equipped and ready to take on big challenges concerning business growth. Fortunately enough, many personal trainers have already been in the position where you are today, and they moved on to become big names in this industry. I was there myself once a couple of decades back. But today, I take pride in telling people about my success journey and every hurdle that came in my life. All of the obstacles helped me shape myself and my career.

Always approach your failures as your lessons and learn from them not to repeat those mistakes in the future. This is why I decided to write books that will help my readers become better trainers – not only in terms of knowledge and skills, but also in terms of conduct, which is the most important of all.

Before we move toward the final part of this chapter, here are some personal tips for how I want my readers to be in their conduct: be yourself. Being professional with clients is important, but nobody would want to work out with a human-machine. Add the element of the human factor, and don't be afraid to laugh and converse with your clients (both new and old). The next thing is to be flexible; your clients have lives outside the gym, and it is only one significant part of the rest of their routine. It is now up to you how you retain them or make them never want to walk in again. If your client has to cancel at the last minute sometimes, roll with it. Of course, if it happens all the time, see the next tip. Another critical aspect of an excellent prospering business is teamwork. Teamwork plays a crucial role in shaping the outcomes of any process. You are a part of a team, and so are the people in your surroundings. Your staff and your clients both form a team with you to achieve their goals. The book contains vital information on topics such as a welcome workout, building connection with the client, helping solve clients' queries, table talk (from floor to the table and finally closing), and recommendations. All of this is a collaborative effort that can be achieved through working in alliance with your team.

To help run your business smoothly, make sure your staff is in sync with the vision, and so are you. At the same time, work together with your clients to help them achieve their desired body goals. To stand out as a fitness trainer, you need not just education but also business and marketing acumen, basic psychology skills, and an outlook to achieve success.

Personal trainers need to know how to stay fit and help others work out, but they should also have a firm grip on understanding sports psychology, rehabilitation, nutrition, sales, health factors, and much more. This book will guide you on how to take in your clients from filling the primary information form to killing their workout routine and achieving their goals. It will help you create workouts for all skill and fitness levels, make a passive income, and grow your career and business. The book is divided into three different sections and entails detailed information on how to treat a client from the moment they walk in through the door to finally signing them to work with you.

Each chapter of this book addresses specific topics and includes actionable advice which will help you take immediate action and implement it soundly. I firmly believe that there lies improvement in these pages for every one of you reading. Not everyone is going to employ the same ideas, but I am positive that each of you will take away something that will improve your life in many different ways.

"If you think lifting is dangerous, try being weak. Being weak is dangerous."

-Bret Contreras, Sports Scientist

I do not restrict fitness to any age group, gender, or race. Everyone needs to be healthy and fit to perform optimally in their everyday lives. I believe if we instill the importance of proper diet and regular exercise in children from an early age, they will grow up in a better environment.

I have been a part of the fitness field for a long time now and have paid my services both as a trainee and a trainer. I know the ins and outs of this industry and have thoroughly assessed it in terms of qualitative and quantitative analysis. I want to equip the readers with authentic knowledge that I have gained through extensive research and broad experience over the last two decades.

My team and I specialize in outcome-driven, effective methods of training, exercise, nutrition, and supplementation and education for clients and personal trainers alike. This book will provide you with essential tips on health and fitness. It will also direct you through some of the most overlooked loopholes.

The world is changing at a rapid pace; we are evolving and advancing in every field, but it seems like with fitness and health, we are stuck with age-old principles. We need to adapt to the advancing surroundings to always stay ahead of our competition and make our business thrive.

"Success usually comes to those who are too busy to be looking for it."

-Henry David Thoreau, poet, and philosopher

Made in the USA
San Bernardino, CA
16 July 2020